EGON RONAY'S

Minutes
from the
Motorway

M25
AROUND LONDON
GUIDE

FOOD &
ACCOMMODATION

Over 200
recommendations

Head of Editorial Moyra Fraser
Editor Michèle Roche
Chief copywriters Diana Artley
                      Peter Long
Editorial contributor Ian Powys
Publisher William Halden

Cover design Carole Thomas & Associates
Page design Suzanne Sykes

Photographs supplied by the AA Photo Library (unless
otherwise stated).

Maps produced by the Cartographic Department of the
Automobile Association.

The contents of this book are believed correct at the time of
printing. Nevertheless, the publisher can accept no respon-
sibility for errors or omissions or changes in the details
given.

Distributed in the United Kingdom by the Publishing Division
of The Automobile Association, Fanum House, Basingstoke, Hampshire RG21 2EA and overseas by the British
Tourist Authority, Thames Tower, Black's Road, London
W6 9EL

ISBN 0 86145 602 5

AA Ref 54483

Typeset, printed and bound in Great Britain by
William Clowes Limited, Beccles and London

Establishment research conducted by a team of full-time
professional inspectors, who are trained to achieve common standards of judgement with as much objectivity as
this field allows. Their professional identities are not
disclosed until they seek information from the management
after paying their bills. The Guide is independent in its
editorial selection and does not accept advertising, pay-
ment or hospitality from the establishments covered.

Egon Ronay's Guides
Second Floor, Greencoat House,
Francis Street, London SW1P 1DH

Contents

How to use this Guide

ORDER OF LISTINGS
Establishments are listed in alphabetical order by location under the nearest, or most convenient, junction exit.

MAP REFERENCES
Map references are to the map section at the front of the book. The map reference is followed by concise directions from the M25 to the establishment.

PRICES

Accommodation
We print categories from A–F rather than actual prices. These are based on the current price, including VAT (also service if applicable), for a double room for two occupants with private bath and cooked breakfast. *PUB (B & B)* prices, however, may not always include private bath.

£A over £110	Where our calculations show
£B £85 to £110	the price to be just above
£C £65 to £85	or below the borderline
£D £50 to £65	between two categories we
£E £35 to £50	symbolise the price as,
£F under £35	for example, £C/D.

Food
About £. . . for two indicates the approximate cost in a *RESTAURANT* of a three-course meal including wine, coffee, service and VAT. This is based on a choice from average-priced dishes on the menu and includes one of the least expensive bottles of wine. Where set menus are offered this is denoted by Set L or Set D, followed by their respective prices.

Two **typical prices** are listed, valid at the time of our visit, for each *JUST A BITE* and *PUB(FOOD)* entry. Minimum charges per person are indicated within Just a Bite entries as establishments in this category often employ a minimum charge during busy periods.

GRADING

Hotels
According to their percentage rating, hotels are classified as

De luxe	85–100%
Grade 1	70–84%
Grade 2	50–69%

The percentage shown on a hotel entry is an individual rating arrived at after careful testing, inspection and calculation according to our unique grading system. The size of the hotels and the prices charged are not considered in the grading, nor is the food. **If we recommend meals in a hotel or inn, a separate entry is made for its dining room.**

Inns
These are not graded. We distinguish them from hotels by their more modest nature, usually with respect to the day rooms. For our purposes, an inn is normally either a pub with hotel-style accommodation or a small hotel with a bar and the atmosphere of a pub.

Restaurants

★ We award one to three stars for excellence of cooking.
★★ One star represents cooking much above average, two
★★★ outstanding cooking, and three the best in the land.

We only include restaurants where the cooking comes up to our minimum standards, however attractive the place may be in other respects. We take into account how well the restaurant achieves what it sets out to do as reflected in the menu, decor, prices, publicity, atmosphere – factors that add up to some of the expectation.

Just a Bite

★ Food much above average

Our team of professional inspectors conduct a nationwide quest for 'just a bite', seeking high-quality food at modest prices and selecting only those establishments which meet their rigorous standards of excellence. They avoid full restaurant meals in the traditional sense, concentrating instead on afternoon teas, light meals and snacks. Large chain caterers are not included.

Pubs

★ Bar food much above average

We only include establishments where our team of inspectors found excellent-quality bar food.

SYMBOLS

♀	A house wine that is judged well chosen by our inspectors
▭	An outstanding wine list
☺	A good cheeseboard
☕	Spotlights Just a Bite establishments recommended for good tea
WC	As washroom facilities are sometimes limited in the type of establishment within our Just a Bite category, we use this to indicate where a clean lavatory with soap, towels, paper and running water was found
(Food)	Pubs recommended for bar food
(B&B)	Pubs recommended for accommodation
Check-in	If residents can check in to pubs for accommodation at any time, we print all day; if check-in is restricted, as the publican's free time is traditionally in the afternoon, when he or she is sometimes not available, we print restricted
Family Pubs	Those pubs we suggest as suitable for families (children welcome) are ones that have a room or indoor area where children are allowed whether eating or not. Many pubs will only welcome children if they are eating
Beers	After Beers we list a selection (or all) of the beers currently available, including lagers and cider on draught. Real ale appears if any of the beers can be defined as such

RESTRICTIONS

Any restrictions on children, dogs, smoking, licensing, and limited choice on availability of fare during certain periods, is printed at the end of each entry. It should be noted, however, that many establishments remain flexible on some issues and we only print restrictions for those establishments which have a definite policy in these matters. Many Just a Bite establishments have flexible opening hours because of their small size or remote location and it is therefore advisable to check. It should also be noted that pub opening hours vary throughout the country. Some pubs have a six-day licence. Again it is advisable to check, particularly during Christmas and the New Year.

Meals on Wheels?

It is a scandal that it was necessary to produce this book at all. The strain of driving on motorways is so bad that the least motorists should expect is to have readily available places where they can rest, eat and be refreshed. Ideally, these should be located alongside the motorway itself.

Egon Ronay's Guides have done more than anyone to improve the standards of motorway service stations over the decades. But the basis for this, our first guidebook linked solely to a motorway, is different. This is a guide to the facilities *off* the motorway network, one motorway in particular—the M25, Britain's latest and most ambitious roadwork project ever.

At the time of writing, there are no catering facilities on the M25. By Spring 1987 it is hoped that a cup of tea and refreshments will be available at *one* location only. And that's all. Red tape is constantly delaying other plans.

The Ministry of Transport admits that this is not unusual. 'The M11 motorway', a spokesman told us 'has been open for ten years and still there are no facilities'.

Isn't it absurd that the same Ministry which rushes out criticisms of motorists at every opportunity for driving too fast on motorways, not taking enough care and so on, cannot provide a place for even a brief rest on one of the busiest motorways in the world.

So we have selected – and inspected – over 200 restaurants, cafés, hotels, inns, bistros and tea rooms, all within minutes of the motorway. You will find them listed alphabetically under the nearest motorway junction. Follow the directions given in the entry, which tell you the signs to look out for, roads to follow and local landmarks to reassure you that you are heading in the right direction.

It's just a pity that it was all so necessary.

William Halden, Publisher

STARRED ENTRIES

Two Star Restaurants —
Bray-on-Thames,
   Waterside Inn
East Grinstead,
   Gravetye Manor Restaurant

One Star Restaurants —
Maidenhead,
   Fredrick's Hotel Restaurant
Old Hatfield,
   Salisbury

Windsor,
   Oakley Court, Oak Leaf Room

Starred Tearooms —
Berkhamsted,
   Cook's Delight
Kew,
   Original Maids of Honour

Starred Pubs —
Chenies,
   Bedford Arms

AFTERNOON TEAS

The following establishments are particularly recommended for afternoon tea as they also merit our teapot symbol for a good – above-average – cuppa.

Amersham,
   Fripps
Berkhamsted,
   Cook's Delight
Compton,
   Old Congregational
   Tea Shop
Guildford,
   Richoux

Kew,
   Original Maids of Honour
Penshurst,
   Fir Tree House Tea
   Rooms
Windsor,
   Windsor Chocolate
   House

DELUXE AND GRADE 1 HOTELS

86% Taplow,
   Cliveden
84% Windsor,
   Oakley Court
81% East Grinstead,
   Gravetye Manor
79% Maidenhead,
   Fredrick's
77% Hayes,
   Sheraton Skyline
76% Ascot,
   Royal Berkshire
   Bagshot,
   Pennyhill Park
   Gatwick Airport,
   Gatwick Hilton
   International

Slough,
   Holiday Inn
73% Ware,
   Briggens Hotel
West Drayton,
   Holiday Inn
71% Hounslow,
   Heathrow Penta
Copthorne,
   Copthorne Hotel
Croydon,
   Holiday Inn
Horley,
   Gatwick Penta
70% Dorking,
   Burford Bridge

Egham,
  Great Fosters
Egham,
  Runnymede

West Drayton,
  Post House
West Drayton,
  Sheraton-Heathrow

BEAUTIFULLY SITUATED HOTELS ────

Bagshot,
  Pennyhill Park
East Grinstead,
  Gravetye Manor
Egham,
  Great Fosters
Harrow Weald,
  Grim's Dyke

Newgate Street,
  Ponsbourne
St Albans,
  Sopwell House
Taplow,
  Cliveden
Windsor,
  Oakley Court

COUNTRY HOUSE HOTELS ────

East Grinstead,
  Gravetye Manor

Taplow,
  Cliveden

HOTELS WITH SWIMMING POOLS ────

Indoor ────
Croydon,
  Holiday Inn
Croydon,
  Selsdon Park
East Grinstead,
  Felbridge
Fawkham,
  Brandshatch Place
Gatwick Airport,
  Gatwick Hilton International
Hayes,
  Sheraton Skyline
Hounslow,
  Heathrow Penta
Maidenhead,
  Crest
Slough,
  Holiday Inn
South Mimms,
  Crest
West Drayton,
  Holiday Inn
West Drayton,
  Sheraton-Heathrow

Outdoor ────
Ascot,
  Berystede
Bagshot,
  Pennyhill Park
Croydon,
  Selsdon Park
Dorking,
  Burford Bridge
Dorking,
  White Horse
East Grinstead,
  Felbridge
East Horsley,
  Thatchers
Egham,
  Great Fosters
Hayes,
  Skyway
Horley,
  Chequers Thistle
Horley,
  Post House
Newgate Street,
  Ponsbourne
Redbourn,
  Aubrey Park Hotel

Taplow,
  Cliveden
Ware,
  Briggens

West Drayton,
  Excelsior

HOTELS WITH FISHING, GOLF, RIDING, SQUASH & TENNIS

Fishing
Bagshot,
  Pennyhill Park
Bray-on-Thames,
  Monkey Island
East Grinstead,
  Gravetye Manor
Egham,
  Runnymede
Shorne,
  Inn on the Lake
Taplow,
  Cliveden
Ware,
  Briggens House
Windsor,
  Oakley Court

Golf
Bagshot,
  Pennyhill Park
Croydon,
  Selsdon Park
Ware,
  Briggens House
West Drayton,
  Holiday Inn

Riding
Bagshot,
  Pennyhill Park
Croydon,
  Selsdon Park

Squash
Ascot,
  Royal Berkshire
Cobham,
  Ladbroke Seven Hills
Copthorne,
  Copthorne
Croydon,
  Holiday Inn
Croydon,
  Selsdon Park
Fawkham,
  Brandshatch Place
Horley,
  Gatwick Penta
Maidenhead,
  Crest
Taplow,
  Cliveden

Tennis
Ascot,
  Royal Berkshire
Bagshot,
  Pennyhill Park
Burnham,
  Burnham Beeches
Cobham,
  Ladbroke Seven Hills
Cobham,
  Woodlands Park
Croydon,
  Selsdon Park
Dane End,
  Green End Park
Egham,
  Great Fosters
Fawkham,
  Brandshatch Place
Newgate Street,
  Ponsbourne
Slough,
  Holiday Inn
Taplow,
  Cliveden
Ware,
  Briggens House
West Drayton,
  Holiday Inn

OPEN AIR EATING

Junctions 5–6
5 Hildenborough, *Gate Inn*

Ide Hill, *Cock Inn*

Penshurst, *Fir Tree House Tea Rooms*

Sevenoaks, *Le Chantecler*

6 Kenley, *Wattenden Arms*

Limpsfield, *Limpsfield Brasserie*

Junctions 7–8
7 Horley, *Ye Olde Six Bells*

Junctions 9–10
9 Dorking, *Burford Bridge Hotel Lounge*

10 Cobham, *Plough*

Compton, *Old Congregational Tea Shop*

Effingham, *Plough*

Guildford, *Richoux*

Ripley, *Anchor*

Ripley, *Clock House*

Ripley, *Seven Stars*

Thames Ditton, *Albany*

Thames Ditton, *Skiffers*

West Clandon, *Onslow Arms*

Junctions 11–13
11 Shepperton, *Thames Court*

12 Charlton Village, *Harrow*

Richmond, *Caffe Mamma*

Richmond, *Mrs Beeton*

Richmond, *Refectory*

Richmond, *Wildefoods Wholefood Café*

Twickenham, *Prince Albert*

Twickenham, *White Swan*

13 Ascot, *Royal Berkshire Restaurant*

Ascot, *Stag*

Junctions 14–16
15 Bray, *Crown Inn*

Dorney, *Palmer Arms*

Eton, *Eton Wine Bar*

Windsor, *Dôme*

Junctions 17–18
18 Amersham, *Willow Tree*

Chenies, *Bedford Arms Restaurant & Bar*

Ley Hill, *Swan Inn*

Junctions 19–22
20 Berkhamsted, *Cook's Delight*

21 Harpenden, *Silver Cup*

21a St Albans, *Kingsbury Mill Waffle House*

Junctions 25–27
26 Toot Hill, *Green Man*

SUNDAY EATING

Junctions 1–4
2 Greenwich, *Le Premier Cru* (L)

4 Bromley, *Hollywood Bowl* (D)

Junctions 5–6
5 Ide Hill, *Cock Inn* (L)

Penshurst, *Fir Tree House Tea Rooms* (3–6)

6 East Grinstead,
  Evergreen (D)
  Limpsfield,
  Old Lodge (L)
  South Godstone,
  La Bonne Auberge
  (L)

Junctions 7–8

7 Croydon, *Munbhave*
  Croydon, *Tung Kum*
  East Grinstead,
  Gravetye Manor
  Horley, *Ye Olde Six
  Bells*
8 Chipstead, *Dene
  Farm* (L)
  Walton-on-the-Hill,
  Ebenezer Cottage
  (L)

Junctions 9–10

9 Dorking, *Burford
  Bridge Hotel Lounge*
  East Horsley, *Thatchers
  Hotel Restaurant*
  Surbiton, *Fortunes*
10 Cobham, *Plough*
  Compton, *Old Congre-
  gational Tea Shop*
  East Molesey,
  Langan's Bar & Grill
  East Molesey, *Vecchia
  Roma*
  Esher, *Good Earth*
  Guildford, *Rumwong*
  Ripley, *Anchor* (L)
  Ripley, *Clock House* (L)
  Ripley, *Seven Stars*
  West Clandon, *Onslow
  Arms* (L)

Junctions 11–13

11 Shepperton, *Thames
  Court*
12 Camberley, *Tithas*
  Richmond, *Caffé
  Mamma*
  Richmond, *Mrs Beeton*
  Richmond, *Refectory*
  Richmond, *Richmond
  Harvest*

Richmond, *Wildefoods
  Wholefood Café*
13 Ascot, *Royal Berkshire
  Restaurant*
  Ascot, *Stag*

Junctions 14–16

15 Bray, *Crown Inn* (L)
  Bray-on-Thames,
  Waterside Inn
  Dorney, *Palmer Arms*
  Eton, *Eton Wine Bar*
  Hayes, *Sheraton
  Skyline, Colony
  Room* (D)
  Kew, *Pissaro's*
  Maidenhead, *Fredrick's
  Hotel Restaurant*
  Taplow, *Cliveden
  Dining Room*
  Windsor, *Angelo's
  Wine Bar*
  Windsor, *Dôme*
  Windsor, *Oakley Court,
  Oak Leaf Room*
  Windsor, *Windsor
  Chocolate House*

Junctions 17–18

18 Amersham, *Fripp's*
  Amersham, *Willow Tree*
  Chenies, *Bedford Arms
  Restaurant & Bar*
  Ley Hill, *Swan Inn* (L)

Junctions 19–20

20 Berkhamsted, *Cook's
  Delight*

Junctions 23–24

23 Old Hatfield,
  Salisbury (L)
  Welwyn, *Heath Lodge
  Hotel Restaurant*

Junctions 25–27

25 Hertford, *Marquee*
26 South Woodford,
  Ho-Ho
  Toot Hill, *Green Man*
  Waltham Abbey,
  Blunk's (D)

Fun & Food Off M25

Penshurst Place – Whitbread Hop Farm

Leave the **M25 at Junction 5**. Take the A21 (signposted Hastings) and follow signs for Tonbridge North (B245). Turn right on to B2027 and left just before Penshurst Station on to B2176. This brings you to Penshurst Village.

Penshurst Place, home of the Sidney family and their descendants for more than 400 years, stands in beautiful gardens. The house itself contains the finest 14th Century domestic Hall to survive in Britain; with its Long Gallery, completed in 1607, it will take the visitor through the centuries, in company with the many illustrious personages who have lived in, visited or been associated with Penshurst Place. Here in Penshurst, you should treat yourself to a delicious cream tea at the charming **Fir Tree House Tea Rooms** (see page 53). From Penshurst head back towards Tonbridge to join the A21 for Hastings. Four miles along this road, turn left on to the B2015 towards Maidstone. A couple of miles will bring you to the *Whitbread Hop Farm*. Here, in the largest remaining group of Victorian oast houses, is a museum where the history of hop production is explained. The Hop Farm is also the 'retirement home' for the Whitbread Shire Horses, used for delivering beer in the City of London, and a team of them draw the Lord Mayor in his coach on ceremonial occasions. The farm is open from Easter to late October, 10am until 5pm. Entrance costs £1.50 (75p children).

Leaving the Hop Farm, return to the A21 (Hastings). After five miles fork left on to the A262 which will take you on a tour of picturesque Kentish villages and hop fields – Goudhurst, Sissinghurst, with its garden lovingly created by Victoria Sackville-West in the 1930s, and on to Biddenden for dinner where **Ye Maydes**, located in a row of half-timbered houses in the High Street, offers an imaginative evening menu, coupled with a warm and friendly welcome (see Egon Ronay's Guide 1987 to Hotels, Restaurants & Inns). This lovely little village with its weavers' cottages and mediaeval Cloth Hall is celebrated for its 'Maids' – Siamese twin girls born here in 1500, and who lived here until 1534. They are still remembered each year on Easter Sunday. To return to the M25 go back along the A262 and take the A21 north (London), rejoining the motorway at junction 5.

Bodiam Castle

Leave the **M25 at junction 5** taking the A21 (signposted Hastings). Turn left 4 miles after Penbury on to the A262. Follow the road for about 15 miles. Turn right on to the A28 and follow the road into Tenterden. The *Kent & East*

Penshurst Place, (above) home of the Sidney family for more than 400 years; (left) Bodiam Castle, the last great fortification of castle design in England.

Sussex Steam Railway, runs from Tenterden to Wittersham, at the edge of Romney Marsh. There is an extensive timetable of services from Easter (weekends), and during the summer, with daily services June to August. Out of Tenterden, on the A28 towards Hastings, turn right after six miles on to A268 to Sandhurst; turn left in Sandhurst village for Bodiam.

Bodiam Castle was fortified by Sir Edward Dalyngrigge, with a licence from King Richard II, in 1385. It was designed to defend the area from attacks by the French who, at that time, had control of the Channel and had sacked Winchelsea and Rye; the River Rother, below the castle, was then a navigable estuary. The Castle was, in fact, never put to the test for control over the Channel was re-established. The Castle is the last great fortification of the 300 years of castle design in England, built just as the introduction of gunpowder began to make the mediaeval fortress obsolete. It was intended to be a comfortable home as well as a fortress. Sir Edward incorporated all the latest design ideas from his service in France in Edward III's wars; the domestic buildings, Great Hall and Chapel are an integral part of the castle. Previously, living quarters were put up rather haphazardly within the defensive walls. The Castle is open daily, Easter to October, 10am to 5.30pm, and from 10am to sunset (closed Sundays between November and March). It is closed over the Christmas period, and is occasionally closed to the public due to filming commitments. Admission prices are £1.20 (60p children).

From Bodiam head back towards the A21 and turn left for dinner at the **Bough House** in Robertsbridge in the High Street (see Egon Ronay's Guide 1987 to Hotels, Restaurants & Inns). Olivia Stalker cooks everything to order at this cosy, black-beamed restaurant. Her set-dinner menus offer an imaginative choice, from tagliatelle with a creamy ham and garlic sauce to juicy steak sharply sauced with mustard. Vegetables are superb and sweets simple.

The Historic Tour – Haxted Mill, Hever and Chiddingstone Castles

Leave the **M25 at Junction 6** and travel down the A22 towards East Grinstead for about 5 miles. Turn left after Blindley Heath along an unclassified road to Lingfield and left again for Edenbridge. A couple of miles will bring you to *Haxted Mill*.

Though called a 'Domesday Mill', there was in fact no mill at Haxted in 1086 for the whole area was still covered in oak forest. There was a mill here, however, by 1334 and much of the present building, still on the same site, dates from about 1580. The history of the Mill and the machinery, water-driven and working, is well documented by the Curator.

Leaving the Watermill Museum, head for Edenbridge. Should examining the intricacies of the Mill have sharpened your appetites, you may care to call at **Buffins Restaurant** in the High Street. Here you can enjoy inexpensive home-cooked meals in a friendly and unpretentious atmosphere (see page 57). Immediately after the railway bridge (heading south) turn on to the Hever and Chiddingstone road.

Hever Castle was the childhood home of Anne Boleyn, second wife of Henry VIII and mother of Elizabeth I. It dates back to 1270, but Anne's father made it into a comfortable Tudor home. The castle grounds are open to the public 11am to 6pm April to November (last entry 5pm); the Castle from 12 noon (last entry 5.15pm). Admission prices are £3.20 (£2.00 gardens only); £3.00 (£1.80) for senior citizens and £1.60 (£1.20) for children. Children under 5 admitted free.

Leaving the Castle, continue towards Bough Beech, join the B2027 and follow signs to Chiddingstone. It is about four miles to the village, with its 19th Century *Chiddingstone Castle*, and beautifully preserved half-timbered houses from the 16th and 17th centuries. The Castle houses a varied collection, all the interests of one man, Denys Eyre Bower.

Right: Chiddingstone's superb half-timbered houses, dating from 16th & 17th centuries; below: Wisley, the Royal Horticultural Society Gardens.

Here are Stuart and Jacobite objects – and for the scholar, access to a large collection of period documents. There is an Egyptian collection and the largest collection of Japanese lacquer in private hands outside Japan. Chiddingstone Castle is open to the public from the end of March to the end of September, Wednesday to Saturday 2pm to 5pm; Sundays & Bank holidays 11am to 5pm, also weekends in October. Admission prices are £1.50 (85p children). Children under 5 admitted free.

To return home make your way back to the B2027 and follow signs for Tonbridge, then Sevenoaks (B245). This will take you to the A21 which will lead you back to Junction 5 of the M25.

Wisley Gardens

Leave the **M25 at junction 10**. The *Royal Horticultural Society Gardens* is situated on the A3 near Ripley.

There are 250 acres of garden, in which the public is free to wander. It is a garden of great beauty and interest but also one where both plants and gardeners are 'tried out', developed and trained. Members of the RHS have an advantage over the ordinary visitor for they can bring along their gardening problems, seek solutions, or at least help, which is always available. Plants and fruits, too, can be identified. But even for the non-gardener, there is always something to be admired. There are few more lovely sights than the drifts of spring flowers in the Wild Garden, or the Heather Garden in its autumn and winter colours. Perhaps the non-gardener derives even more pleasure from the sheer beauty of the place, whereas the would-be amateur gardener leaves just that little bit frustrated! There are roses, the Formal Garden, the Walled Garden, the Wild Garden, the Summer Garden, Trial Grounds, a Pinetum, an Arboretum, a rock garden, mixed borders and the greenhouses – surely here will be something to interest everyone. There are demonstration areas too, where the awesome size of Wisley and the RHS are brought down to a scale we can all understand – the herb garden, or a garden for the disabled, a small vegetable plot, and ideas about what to plant as ground cover to keep the weeds at bay.

Routes have been prepared at Wisley which allow visitors in wheelchairs, and those who are unable to walk very well, to reach most parts of the gardens without having to negotiate steps. A plan is available from the gatekeeper, on arrival. The Gardens are open every day of the year, except Christmas Day, from 10am on weekdays and 2pm on Sundays, and close at 7pm (or dusk). Entrance on a Sunday morning is reserved for members of the RHS. Tickets cost £3.50 (£3.00 children), and it should be noted that no dogs are allowed.

Refreshment can be found not very far away in Ripley village at the **Anchor**, a traditional village pub serving real ale and homely food – excellent pies (see page 92).

Stratfield Saye

Leave the **M25 at Junction 12** and take the M3 towards Basingstoke. After 20 miles, at Junction 5, exit for Hook (B3349). One mile through Hook, turn left (signposted Lyde/Newnham) and half a mile along this road you will see the **Coach & Horses** on your left. You may see the yellow and black Daimler hearse, which is the pub's official transport, parked outside. Landlady, Mrs Williams is a welcoming host at this friendly family pub, where a good selection of real ales are on offer together with a menu of hearty, satisfying, home-cooked food, prepared by Mrs Williams' son, Liam. (See Egon Ronay's Pub Guide 1987.)

On leaving the pub, continuing in the direction you were going when you arrived, head for the A33. Turn right towards Reading and after a couple of miles turn left for Stratfield Saye. One mile down this road is *Stratfield Saye House*.

Stratfield Saye dates from the reign of Charles I and was bought by the Duke of Wellington in 1817; the same year that he bought Apsley House in London, using some of the £600,000 voted to him by a grateful nation after Waterloo. Instead of re-building, as had been his original intention, the Duke modernised the old house, installing central heating and blue-patterned china 'water closets' in the rooms. Stratfield Saye has been the home of the Dukes of Wellington ever since. It houses a collection of paintings, memorabilia and objects of interest relating to the first Duke and his campaigns. In the museum is the immense carriage that was used at his funeral. The house is open to the public over Easter and on Saturdays and Sundays only in April. Open daily 11.30am–5pm from May to end September.

Signs just outside the House gates will direct you to the *Wellington Country Park*, further along the B3349. Here the family can find facilities for boating, fishing, camping and riding. There are nature trails, an adventure playground and a miniature steam railway. Open daily from March to October and on winter weekends between 10am and dusk.

After such a full day out, you might need to try more of the fare on offer at the **Coach & Horses** on your way back to the M25. To coin a phrase, it could 'mérite un détour'.

Statfield Saye, home of the Dukes of Wellington since 1817, when it was acquired by the Duke of Wellington as a reward for his victory at Waterloo.

Royal Windsor & Surroundings

Leave the **M25 at junction 13** and follow signs for Windsor (A308). You will drive alongside the Watermeadow at Runnymede, where the Barons forced a reluctant King John to sign Magna Carta in 1215. Nearby are two memorials, one to the Commonwealth Air Forces, the other to President Kennedy. Both are clearly signposted, should you wish to visit them. There is so much to see and do in Windsor that it is hard to know where to begin. Why not plan your visit over a glass of wine in **Tracks Brasserie & Wine Bar** underneath Central Station? An unusual location which makes an interesting setting for this friendly establishment offering tasty home-cooked lunches and suppers (see page 132).

Is it raining? Is it a day for outdoor pursuits? Have you got the kids with you? Here are a few suggestions.

Windsor Castle, clustered about the Round Tower and the two baileys, erected by William the Conqueror, has grown with successive monarchs and is the largest inhabited castle in the world. The town itself, which like the Castle has also grown over the centuries, is mainly Georgian and Victorian in design and architecture. Within the Precincts are the State Apartments, which you can visit when the Queen is not in residence (if the Royal Standard is flying on the Round Tower you are out of luck!), and St. George's Chapel where the annual Garter Ceremony is held, the Dolls' House which belonged to Queen Mary, and an exhibition of drawings by Leonardo da Vinci and Holbein. There are the Royal Mews to be visited, also. The Precincts are open daily (except for the Garter Ceremony in June) from 10am to 7.15pm, but close earlier during certain periods (March to April and September to March). All admission times to the Castle are subject to alteration, depending not only upon the season but also upon Royal occasions and engagements. However, 10.30am until dusk is the normal span. Check on arrival and plan accordingly.

If the weather is fine, then explore the Great Park. It is open every day of the year, sunrise to sunset, and well-kept footpaths will take you through most of the five thousand acres of what was formerly the Royal hunting forest. Herne the Hunter still hunts here on stormy nights!

You may have shopping to do as well as sightseeing, and will enjoy exploring the King Edward Court Shopping Centre. After you have made your purchases, the **Windsor Chocolate House**, a traditional tea house-cum-shop, near the Castle, is a welcome retreat for light refreshment or lunch (see page 132).

Royalty & Railways – on a permanent site in Central Station, immediately above **Tracks** where you are planning your day, is an exhibition re-creating the pomp and splendour of Queen Victoria's Diamond Jubilee in 1897. The Royal Train has brought honoured guests from Germany and Russia and the Coldstream Guards are there to welcome them. All the figures made by Madame Tussauds are extremely lifelike, and sound effects add to the impression of realism. In addition there is a 15 minute theatre show and a slide presentation, which takes you through the achievements of Queen Victoria's 'Sixty Glorious Years'. Open daily, except Christmas Day, from 9.30am until 5.30pm (4.30pm in winter).

Windsor Safari Park, situated along the B3022 to the south-west of the town, is open daily from 10am until 5.45pm (3pm October–Easter). It is closed Christmas Day, the only day of the year when the kids will not be able to enjoy the antics of the dolphins, or watch the elephants, lions and llamas.

Back along the A308, by which you came into Windsor, are

Royalty & Empire: Queen Victoria by Madame Tussauds. Relive, sixty glorious years of Queen Victoria's memorable reign on permanent exhibition at Windsor & Eton railway station, Windsor.

courtesy of Royalty & Empire

courtesy of Thorpe Park

Above: Wilde Water River Rapid Ride, Thorpe Park, a major new ride for 1987; right: The Woodland in May, Savill Garden.

Miss Lyn Randall

the *Savill and Valley Gardens*. The Savill Garden lies along the eastern boundary of Windsor Great Park. Like the Great Park, it was created by drainage and landscaping during the reigns of King George II and King George III. But it was after Eric Savill, who took up the post of Surveyor and later became Deputy Ranger, that the garden was named in 1951 by order of King George VI. Sir Eric Savill died in 1980, just before the Golden Jubilee of the Gardens was celebrated. Rhododendrons flowering in May are the main attraction here but there is something to be seen at all times of the year in the thirty or so acres of Savill Garden, or in the Valley Gardens, bordering on Virginia Water, along the A30 Camberley–Egham road. The Valley Garden is open daily, sunrise to sunset, and there is no charge for admission.

Thorpe Park, close to junction 12 of the M25 (junction 2 of the M3) is really *the* place for the 'family day out' with a 'Pay One Price' system which means that the cost of nearly all rides, attractions, exhibits and shows is included. Only roller skate hire and watersport amusements have extra charges. Thorpe Park opens on 12 April 1987 from 10am until 6pm (till 8pm in high season) but is closed on weekdays during most of May and September.

Whipsnade Park & The Shuttleworth Collection

Leave the **M25 at Junction 21**, and head north on the M1. There are two good trips up this way, both for parents and the kids, and each is worth a half day at the very least.

Whipsnade Park Zoo was created long before the idea of Safari Parks and Dolphinaria became popular and, probably, it is still Britain's greatest open Zoo. Take Junction 9 off the M1 and head along the A5; turn off left on to the B4540. Whipsnade is open daily, except Christmas Day (try a visit on Boxing Day for the animals are delighted to see someone again after their lonely Christmas!). Opening times are 10am until 6pm (or sunset, whichever is the earlier) on weekdays, and 10am until 7pm on Sundays and Bank Holidays. Entrance costs £3.20 (£1.60 children and senior citizens). Here you can take a train ride through the 'African Veldt' or the 'Asian Plains'. At peak periods it's a steam train; otherwise you will have to make do with a diesel! Animal feeding times, too, are an attraction: lions 3.30pm; tigers 3.45pm; penguins 4.15pm (all one hour earlier October–March). Some of the world's rarest and most threatened species live and breed in contented safety here. Among them cheetahs, white rhinos and the Przewalski's wild horses.

Back on to the M1, head north and follow signs to Woburn where you might like to stop for lunch at the welcoming **Black Horse Inn** in Bedford Street. This former coaching inn, offering real ale, does a tasty menu of bar snacks and a good range of salads and buffet dishes which you can enjoy in an attractive walled garden on fine days. Children are welcome. (See Egon Ronay's Pub Guide 1987.)

After lunch rejoin the M1 to junction 13, then take the A421 towards Bedford. Skirt round to the south of the town, take the A603 to Sandy to join the A1 heading south. From Biggleswade, signs will direct you to the *Old Warden Aerodrome*, home of the Shuttleworth Collection of Historic Aeroplanes and Road Vehicles.

The Collection is housed on the estate of the Shuttleworth family who made their fortune developing steam farm machinery in the 1840s. Richard, who inherited the estate in 1932 was a racing driver and began collecting aeroplanes, starting with a 1909 Bleriot. He joined the RAF and was tragically killed in a night-flying accident in 1940. His mother endowed the Collection in his memory after the war. The Collection is unique in the world, aiming to keep the exhibits in their original condition but to maintain as many as possible in full flying order. At Old Warden you can see much of the history and development of aviation from Bleriot, through the Bristol Fighter and SE5 of the First World War, to Gloster Gladiator and Spitfire. Flying displays are normally held April to October on the last Sunday of each month. Old Warden Aerodrome and the Collection is open (except Christmas and New Year) from 10.30am until 5.30pm (4.30pm in winter).

The LVG CVI, a German bombing and reconnaissance plane introduced around 1918 and brought over to England after the 1st World War. Part of Shuttleworth Collection since 1966.

Admission to hangars and to minor events is £2.00 (£1.00 children, students and senior citizens). There are several major events during each year – special flying displays, twilight flying displays and the Veteran Aero Model days. Prices for these are announced in the Press six weeks before the event. A phone call on (076727) 288 will establish what is on and what the admission charge is.

Richard Shuttleworth also collected many early motor cars and these, too, are on display. Among them are a 2-cylinder Daimler of 1897, the Panhard Levassor which King Edward VII drove to Ascot in 1898, early bicycles and the Fire Engine from nearby Ampthill from 1913.

Back home? You have the choice of the M1 back to Junction 21 or coming back down the A1/A1M through Stevenage and Hatfield, rejoining the M25 at Junction 23.

Waltham Abbey & Epping Forest

Leave the **M25 at Junction 26**. A couple of miles drive along the A121 brings you to *Waltham Abbey*. The Abbey was founded in 1030, and it was here that King Harold's mains were buried after the Battle of Hastings. The Abbey was much restored in the 1860s, and it is from this time that the Jesse Window dates. This was designed by Sir Edward Burne-Jones and is a fine example of 19th century stained glass.

Here in Waltham Abbey you might care to sample the long list of expertly prepared French dishes at **Blunk's** in Market Square. Seafood features strongly on the imaginative menu, with delights like Sole Newburg and a very fine coquille de fruits de mer. Meat dishes might include beef Stroganoff and breast of chicken with a whisky-dipped sauce (see page 164).

Fun & Food

Most of the forests which covered England in Norman times have long since disappeared but *Epping Forest* survived and was given in perpetuity to her people by Queen Victoria in 1878. But it was by Henry VIII's order that the Hunting Lodge at Chingford was built. Epping Forest was one of his favourite hunting preserves. He used Waltham Abbey as a base from which to go into the Forest, but felt a more permanent lodge was needed and decreed that a new Royal Park should be made at Fairmead, near today's Chingford. Drive south from Waltham along the A112 into Chingford turning left on to the A110 and left again into King's Head Hill. A couple of miles will bring you to the Royal Forest Hotel, and immediately alongside this mock-Tudor building is the *Hunting Lodge*.

The Hunting Lodge, home of the Epping Forest Museum, has been carefully restored to resemble its original form as closely as possible. One exception is the upper floors; originally unglazed and used to obtain a grandstand view of the chase, they are now glazed and form part of the Museum – although the floors still slope outwards from the centre to enable rain water to run off freely! The museum is open Wednesdays to Sundays, 2pm until 6pm (or dusk) and the entrance fee is 25 pence.

On this route you will have passed through much of present day Epping Forest, between Waltham and Chingford. Before leaving the area, though, you may like to see the little Saxon church of St Andrew at Greensted. Go back up to Waltham, turn east along the M25 to the M11 turn-off. After four miles, take the A414 signposted Chelmsford. Three miles further on, turn right into Blake Hall Road, a small country lane which

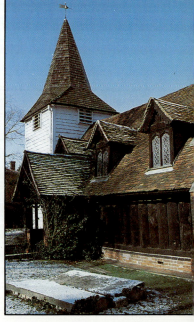

St Andrew's Church (interior & exterior) Greensted: the only surviving Saxon church with original nave walls made from oak.

brings you to Greensted. *St Andrew's Church* is the only surviving Saxon church with original nave walls, made from huge oak logs split lengthwise with the flat surfaces turned inwards. It was probably erected about 845 AD although there is evidence of a smaller building on the site of the Chancel, built in the 7th century. The oak trees used to build this little church might, perhaps, have been acorns when Christ was alive! You are in a place of worship that spans the history of Christianity.

Take the little road through Toot Hill back to the M25 and if you chose to bypass Blunk's you might try lunch at the **Green Man**, a pleasant creeper-clad pub with plenty of choice from soups and sandwiches to salads and some adventurous hot dishes (see page 163).

Artists' Food Trail

Leave the **M25 at Junction 28** and head for Colchester along the A12. This, the oldest town in Britain, has a lot of interest, but today pass by, and 43 miles from the junction, take the turning towards Dedham.

It is *'Constable Country'* where you begin your tour. If it is time for lunch, and your intention is not to do *too* much touring, then in Dedham you have plenty of choice! At the **Dedham Vale Hotel**, a substantial buffet lunch is served in the stylish **Terrace** restaurant; in the Conservatory area, spit roasts and grills are prepared. (See Egon Ronay's Guide 1987 to Hotels, Restaurants & Inns.) However, for a quick morning coffee, visit the **Essex Rose Tea House** in Royal Square. Not only can Mr Bower and his handmaidens serve you good coffee and tempting cakes, but he is a fount of knowledge about the area. Set teas are the main attraction here but light lunches are also available with hot specials of the day in winter (see Egon Ronay's Just a Bite Guide 1987).

The artist **John Constable**, was born in East Bergholt nearby and attended the local Dedham schoolhouse. His father owned Flatford Mill, where Constable painted 'The Hay Wain' and 'Willy Lott's Cottage'. You can hire a rowing boat and work off your lunch between Dedham and Flatford Mill, or take a walk along the towpath.

Sir Alfred Munnings, the 20th century artist renowned for his paintings of horses, also lived at Dedham and Castle House still contains many of his paintings. Open 2pm until 5pm May to October on Sundays, Wednesdays and Bank Holidays, also Thursdays and Saturdays during August.

Leaving Dedham for East Bergholt, the one-way road system brings you to the Church. Stop if you have the time, to see the unique timber-framed belfry, on the ground in the churchyard. From East Bergholt take the B1070 to Hadleigh. All the villages through which you pass have timber-framed houses, typical of the 14th–16th centuries, coloured to complement the landscape in terra cotta, cream pink and buff. The Guildhall at Hadleigh, on the Green by the Church, merits a visit. It is a fine 15th Century building – but come on

Above: Lavenham, the Guildhall built in the mid 16th century; below: Kersey, one of Suffolk's most attractive villages and an important centre of the woollen industry in 14th and 15th centuries.

a Thursday if you wish to see inside for it is only open then. Head out of Hadleigh across the River Brett on A1141 to Lavenham. Make a short detour following signs to Kersey and Lindsey. Kersey, like nearby Lindsey, gave its name to a type of woollen cloth in the 14th and 15th centuries and it is probably the gem of all the Suffolk villages you will see on this tour, outstanding even in this area of picturesque charm. Lavenham is a fine example of a town which grew to prosperity on its wool trade; little has changed since. It is a village of exceptionally beautiful timber-framed houses. It has a church rivalling many cathedrals in grandeur, with a 140 ft tower constructed in local knapped flint.

From Lavenham continue along the B1071 for five miles to Sudbury, birthplace of *Thomas Gainsborough*. His home at 46 Gainsborough Street now houses a museum and Arts Centre. *Charles Dickens* brought less welcome notoriety to Sudbury when he used it as 'Eatanswill' in his 'Pickwick Papers'. Excellent fare can be had at **Ford's** bistro furnished with old church pews. Blackboard daily specials could include delicious smoked haddock mousse, eggs florentine and mixed grill kebab. Superb baking too. (See Egon Ronay's Just a Bite Guide 1987.)

From Sudbury take the A134 back towards Colchester and then head for London on the A12. This will lead you to junction 28 of the M25. The whole day will have taken you just over 100 miles through some of the most picturesque and unspoilt East Anglian countryside within easy reach of London.

Maps one and two show the entire route of the M25, plus all the 24-hour petrol service stations which lie within easy reach of the junctions.

On maps three and four all the orbital routes around London are highlighted together with the major interconnecting A and B roads. The exit signs illustrated show road numbers and important destinations, but the distances given are AA mileage figures and do not appear on the actual signs.

Following on from this are 11 pages of detailed maps featuring the M25 junctions and locating recommended restaurants, hotels and pubs. A colour-coded key map to these maps is shown below.

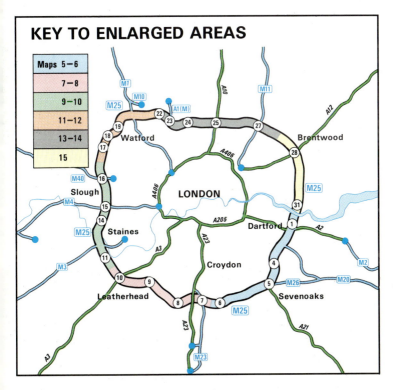

KEY TO ENLARGED AREAS

| Maps | 5—6 |
| 7—8 |
| 9—10 |
| 11—12 |
| 13—14 |
| 15 |

LEGEND TO ENLARGED AREAS

——— Section of Specified Motorway	——— Primary Route
——— Other Motorway	——— A ' Road
——— Dual Carriageway	——— B ' Road
	Burnham Gazetteer Entry

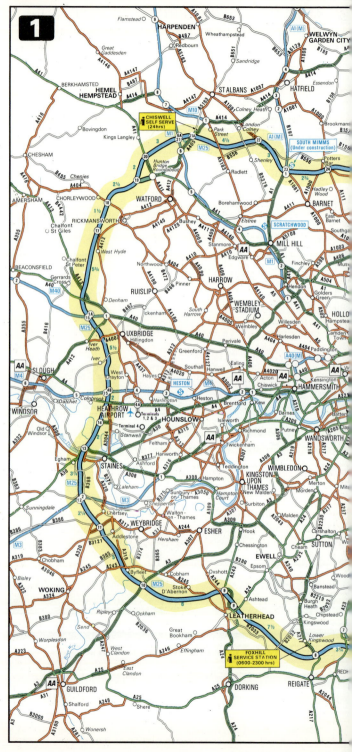

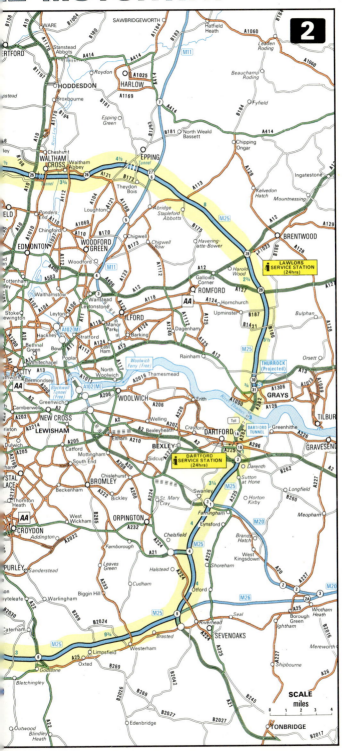

2

M25: MOTORWAY

3

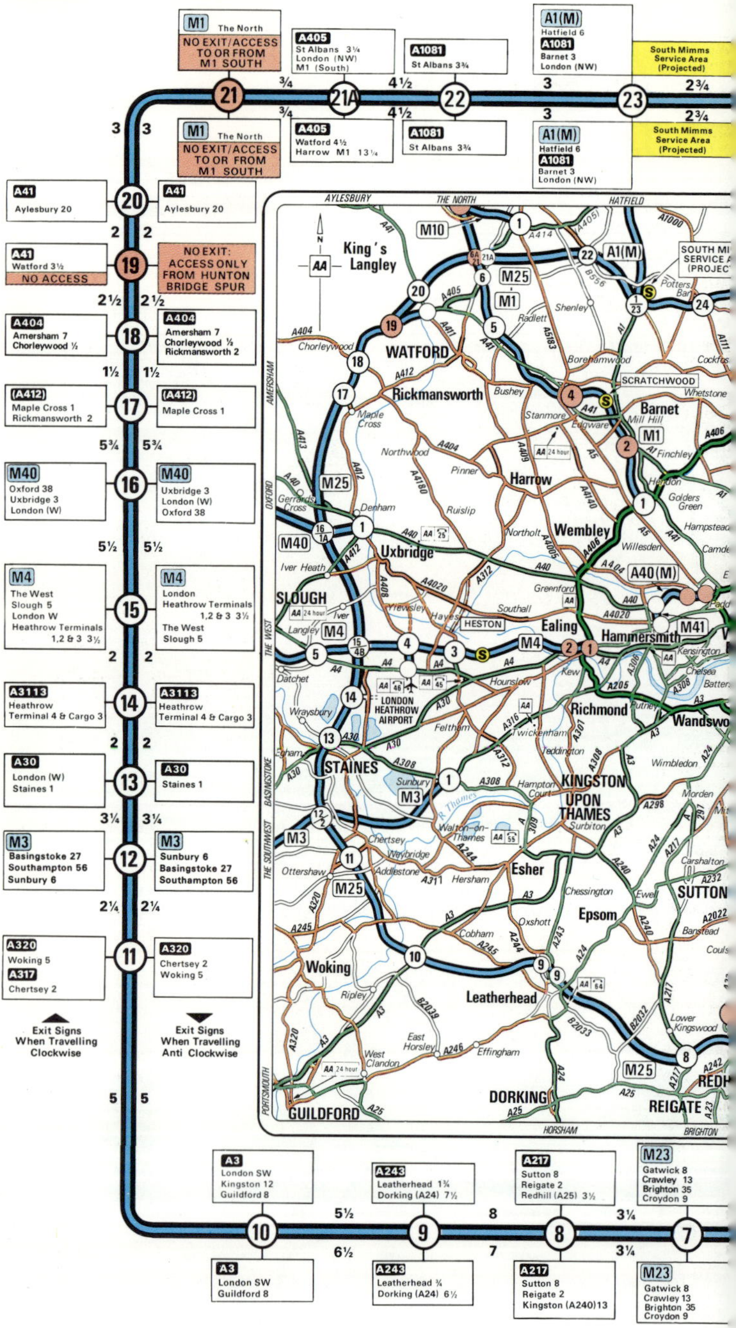
M1 The North
NO EXIT/ACCESS TO OR FROM M1 SOUTH
A405 St Albans 3¼ London (NW) M1 (South)
A405 Watford 4½ Harrow M1 13¼
A1081 St Albans 3¾
A1(M) Hatfield 6 A1081 Barnet 3 London (NW)
South Mimms Service Area (Projected)
21 21A 22 23
¾ 4½ 3 2¾
A41 Aylesbury 20
20
A41 Watford 3½ NO ACCESS
19
NO EXIT: ACCESS ONLY FROM HUNTON BRIDGE SPUR
A404 Amersham 7 Chorleywood ½
A404 Amersham 7 Chorleywood ½ Rickmansworth 2
18
(A412) Maple Cross 1 Rickmansworth 2
(A412) Maple Cross 1
17
M40 Oxford 38 Uxbridge 3 London (W)
M40 Uxbridge 3 London (W) Oxford 38
16
M4 The West Slough 5 London W Heathrow Terminals 1,2 & 3 3½
M4 London Heathrow Terminals 1,2 & 3 3½ The West Slough 5
15
A3113 Heathrow Terminal 4 & Cargo 3
14
A30 London (W) Staines 1
A30 Staines 1
13
M3 Basingstoke 27 Southampton 56 Sunbury 6
M3 Sunbury 6 Basingstoke 27 Southampton 56
12
A320 Woking 5 A317 Chertsey 2
A320 Chertsey 2 Woking 5
11
Exit Signs When Travelling Clockwise
Exit Signs When Travelling Anti Clockwise
3 2 2½ 1½ 5¾ 5½ 2 2 3¼ 2¼ 5
A3 London SW Kingston 12 Guildford 8
A3 London SW Guildford 8
10
A243 Leatherhead 1¾ Dorking (A24) 7½
A243 Leatherhead ¾ Dorking (A24) 6½
9
A217 Sutton 8 Reigate 2 Redhill (A25) 3½
A217 Sutton 8 Reigate 2 Kingston (A240) 13
8
M23 Gatwick 8 Crawley 13 Brighton 35 Croydon 9
7
5½ 6½ 8 7 3¼
AYLESBURY
THE NORTH
HATFIELD
AMERSHAM
OXFORD
THE WEST
BASINGSTOKE
THE SOUTHWEST
PORTSMOUTH
HORSHAM
BRIGHTON
King's Langley
WATFORD
Rickmansworth
Chorleywood
Maple Cross
Northwood
Pinner
Harrow
Ruislip
Denham
Gerrards Cross
Uxbridge
Iver Heath
SLOUGH
Langley
Iver
Yiewsley
Hayes
HESTON
Southall
Greenford
Northolt
Wembley
Willesden
Ealing
Hammersmith
Kensington
Chelsea
Battersea
Datchet
Wraysbury
LONDON HEATHROW AIRPORT
Hounslow
Feltham
Twickenham
Teddington
Richmond
Putney
Wandsworth
Wimbledon
Egham
STAINES
Sunbury
Hampton Court
KINGSTON UPON THAMES
Surbiton
Morden
Chertsey
Weybridge
Addlestone
Ottershaw
Walton-on-Thames
Hersham
Esher
Chessington
Epsom
Ewell
SUTTON
Carshalton
Banstead
Oxshott
Cobham
Woking
Ripley
Leatherhead
East Horsley
West Clandon
Effingham
GUILDFORD
DORKING
Lower Kingswood
REIGATE
Radlett
Shenley
Borehamwood
Bushey
Stanmore
Edgware
Mill Hill
Barnet
Finchley
Hendon
Golders Green
Hampstead
Camden
Potters Bar
Cockfosters
Whetstone
SCRATCHWOOD
SOUTH MIMMS SERVICE AREA (PROJECTED)
R. Thames
Kew
M25 M1 M10 M40 M4 M3 M41 A1(M) A40(M) M23

EXIT SIGNS

4

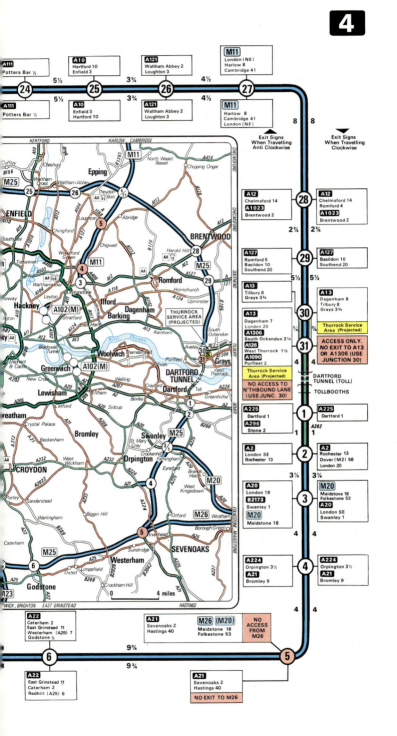

A111
Potters Bar ½

5½

24

A10
Hertford 10
Enfield 3

3¾

25

A121
Waltham Abbey 2
Loughton 3

4½

26

M11
London (NE)
Harlow 8
Cambridge 41

27

8 **8**

A111
Potters Bar ½

5½

A10
Enfield 10
Hertford 10

3¾

A121
Waltham Abbey 2
Loughton 3

4½

M11
Harlow 8
Cambridge 41
London (NE)

Exit Signs
When Travelling
Anti Clockwise

Exit Signs
When Travelling
Clockwise

A12
Chelmsford 14
Romford 4
A1023
Brentwood 2

28

2¾ **2¾**

A12
Chelmsford 14
Romford 4
A1023
Brentwood 2

A127
Romford 5
Basildon 10
Southend 20

29

A127
Basildon 10
Southend 20

5½ **5½**

A13
Tilbury 8
Grays 3¾

A13
Dagenham 8
Tilbury 8
Grays 3¾

30

A13
Dagenham 7
London 20
A1306
South Ockendon 3¼
A126
West Thurrock 1½
A1090
Purfleet 2

31

¾ **¾**

Thurrock Service
Area (Projected)

ACCESS ONLY.
NO EXIT TO A13
OR A1306 (USE
JUNCTION 30)

Thurrock Service
Area (Projected)

NO ACCESS TO
N'THBOUND LANE
(USE JUNC. 30)

4 **4**

DARTFORD
TUNNEL (TOLL)

TOLLBOOTHS

A225
Dartford 1
A296
Stone 2

1

A225
Dartford 1

A282

1

A2
London SE
Rochester 13

2

A2
Rochester 13
Dover (M2) 58
London 20

3¼ **3¼**

A20
London 19
B2173
Swanley 1
M20
Maidstone 18

3

M20
Maidstone 18
Folkestone 53
A20
London SE
Swanley 1

4 **4**

A224
Orpington 3½
A21
Bromley 9

4

A224
Orpington 3½
A21
Bromley 9

4 **4**

A22
Caterham 2
East Grinstead 11
Westerham (A25) 7
Godstone ¼

A21
Sevenoaks 2
Hastings 40

M26 (M20)
Maidstone 18
Folkestone 53

NO
ACCESS
FROM
M26

9¾

6

5

9¾

A22
East Grinstead 11
Caterham 2
Redhill (A25) 6

A21
Sevenoaks 2
Hastings 40

NO EXIT TO M26

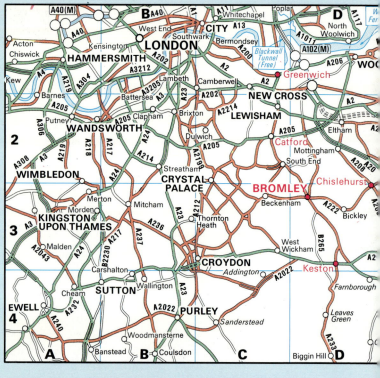

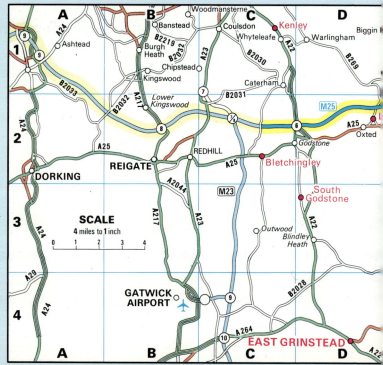

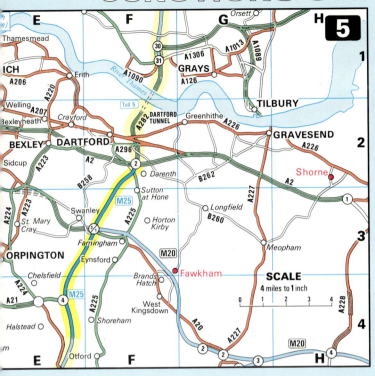

5

Thamesmead
E F G H
Orsett
ICH
A206 Erith
A1090 30 A1306 A1013 A1089
31 GRAYS
A126 TILBURY
River Thames
Welling A207 Crayford Toll 5 Greenhithe A226 GRAVESEND
Bexleyheath DARTFORD A226
BEXLEY DARTFORD TUNNEL A2
Sidcup A223 A296 Shorne
A2 Darenth B262
A223 B258 2 Sutton A227 Longfield 1
A224 Swanley at Hone B260
St. Mary Horton Meopham
Cray A225 Kirby
Farningham M20
ORPINGTON Eynsford Brands SCALE
Chelsfield Hatch Fawkham 4 miles to 1 inch
A224 M25 West 0 1 2 3 4
A21 4 Kingsdown A228
Halstead Shoreham A20
A225 A227 M20
Otford 2 2 3 4
E F H

6

E Cudham F Otford G H
M26 2 2 3
M25 5 A224 Seal 2A
Riverhead A25 West
A25 Borough Malling
Brasted SEVENOAKS Green Ightham B2016
sfield Westerham A225 A227 Mereworth
B269 Shipbourne 2
B2024 Ide Hill A26 Hadlow Hale
B2026 B269 A227 Street
Edenbridge B245 B2015
B2027 A21 Hildenborough
B2027 TONBRIDGE Paddock
B2028 Penshurst B2176 B2017 Wood
B2026 A26
A264 B2188 A264 A21
A264 TUNBRIDGE
WELLS
E F A26 G H

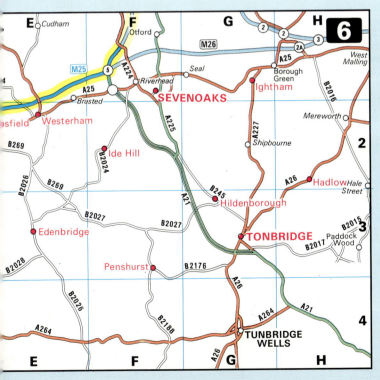

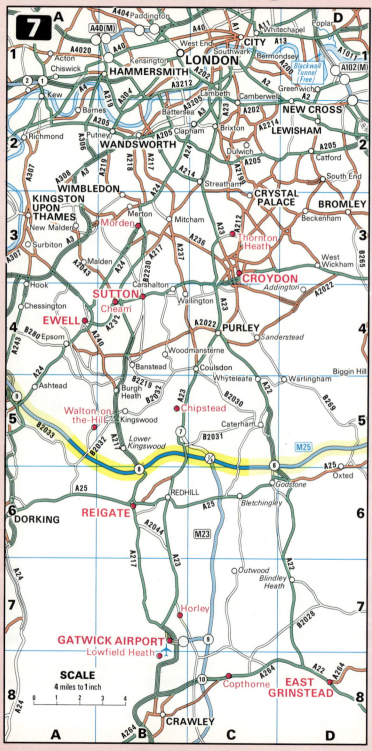

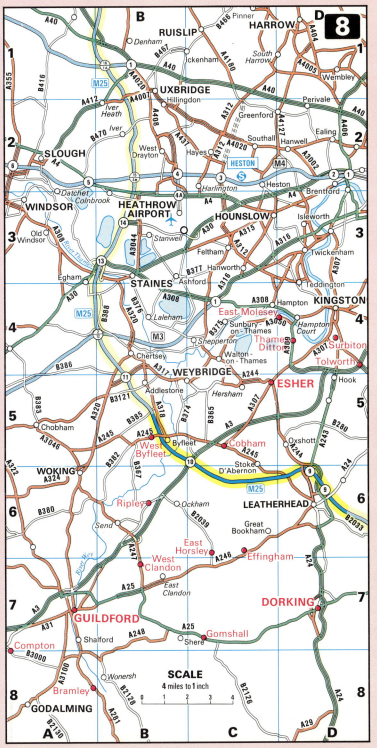

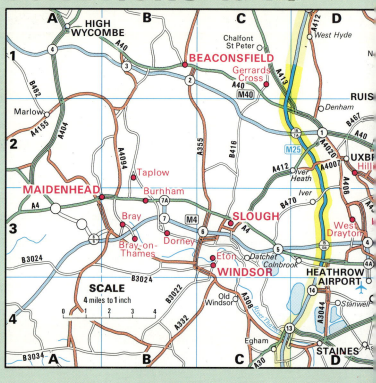

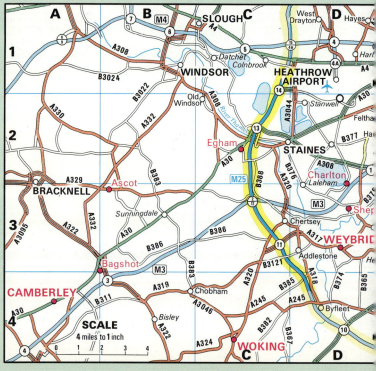

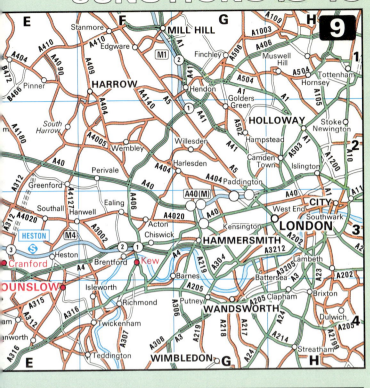

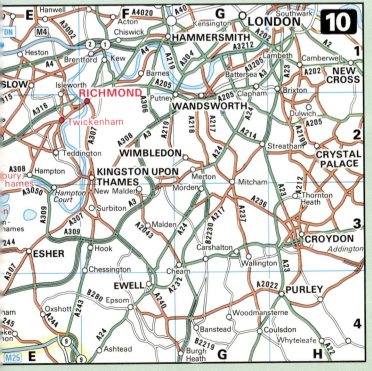

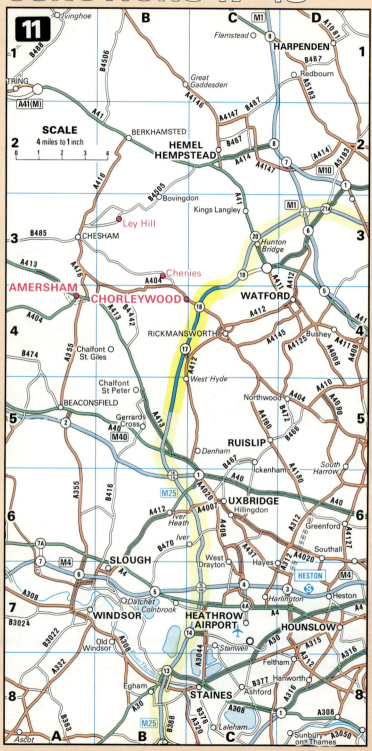

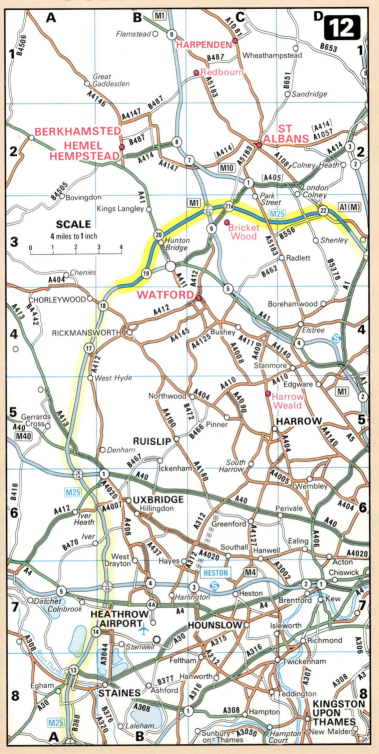

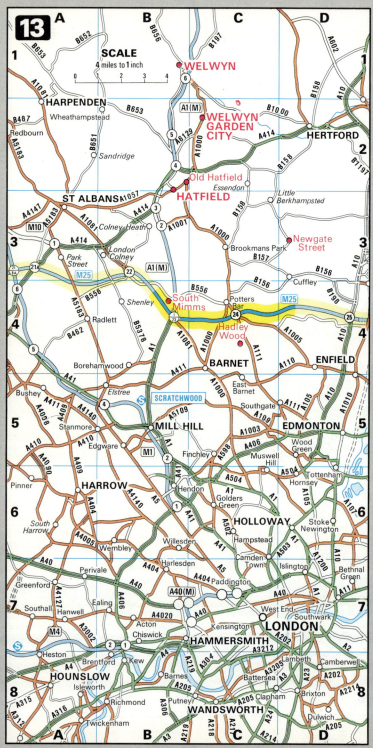

13 **A**

SCALE
4 miles to 1 inch
0 1 2 3 4

B652
B653
B656
B197
WELWYN
A1081
HARPENDEN
Wheathampstead
B653
A1(M)
WELWYN GARDEN CITY
B1000
B158
A10
B487
Redbourn
B651
Sandridge
A6129
A414
HERTFORD
A5183
B158
B1197
A4147
A5183
ST ALBANS
A1057
A414
Old Hatfield
Essendon
HATFIELD
Little Berkhampsted
B158
A1081
A414
Colney Heath
A1001
A1000
Newgate Street
M10
A414
A1000
Brookmans Park
B157
A10
Park Street
London Colney
A1(M)
B156
Cuffley
B156
B198
21A
M25
22
B556
B556
Potters Bar
M25
25
6
A5183
B556
Shenley
South Mimms
Hadley Wood
A5183
Radlett
B462
B5378
A1081
A1000
A1005
A10
Borehamwood
A41
Elstree
SCRATCHWOOD
BARNET
A411
A1000
East Barnet
A111
A110
ENFIELD
Bushey
A411
A4140
A5109
Southgate
A111
A105
A10
A1010
Stanmore
A410
MILL HILL
A1003
EDMONTON
Edgware
A409
A41
M1
Finchley
A598
A406
Wood Green
A504
A410
A409
A41
Hendon
A1
Golders Green
A504
Muswell Hill
Hornsey
Tottenham
A105
A107
Pinner
HARROW
A4140
A5
A41
HOLLOWAY
A502
Stoke Newington
South Harrow
A404
A4005
Wembley
Hampstead
A503
A10
A40
Perivale
A404
Harlesden
A5
Camden Town
Islington
A1200
Bethnal Green
Greenford
A4127
Hanwell
A406
Paddington
A404
A40
A1
A411
Southall
Ealing
A40(M)
West End
Southwark
A2
M4
Heston
A4
Brentford
Kew
A4020
Acton
Chiswick
A40
Kensington
HAMMERSMITH
LONDON
A202
HOUNSLOW
Isleworth
A4
Barnes
A219
A304
A3212
Lambeth
A23
Camberwell
A202
A315
Richmond
A306
Putney
A205
Battersea
A3
Brixton
A2214
A205
Twickenham
A312
A316
WANDSWORTH
A219
A218
A21
A24
A214
Dulwich
A205

A **B** **C** **D**

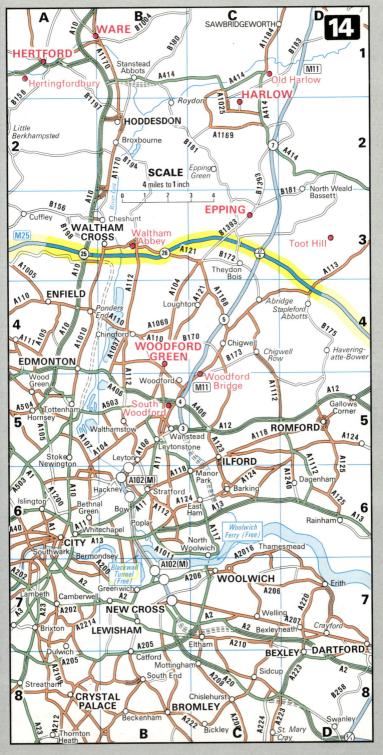

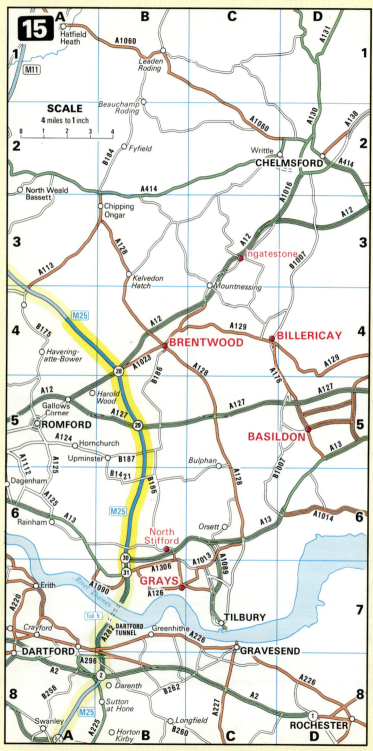

15 A

M11

Hatfield Heath

A1060

Leaden Roding

SCALE
4 miles to 1 inch
0   1   2   3   4

Beauchamp Roding

B184

Fyfield

North Weald Bassett

Chipping Ongar

A414

Writtle

CHELMSFORD

A1060

A130

A138

A414

A1016

A12

A128

A113

Kelvedon Hatch

A12

Mountnessing

Ingatestone

B1007

A12

M25

B175

Havering-atte-Bower

A12

Gallows Corner

ROMFORD

A124

Hornchurch

Upminster

Harold Wood

A127

Brentwood

A1023

B186

A128

A129

BRENTWOOD

BILLERICAY

A129

A176

A127

B187

B14 21

A1112

A125

Dagenham

A125

A13

BASILDON

A127

A13

A128

B1007

Bulphan

M25

B186

Rainham

A13

Orsett

A13

A1014

North Stifford

A1013

A1089

M25

30

31

A1306

A1090

GRAYS

A126

Erith

A220

River Thames

Toll 5

Crayford

A282

DARTFORD TUNNEL

Greenhithe

A226

TILBURY

GRAVESEND

DARTFORD

A2

A296

B258

2

Darenth

B262

Sutton at Hone

A227

A2

A226

M25

Swanley

A225

Horton Kirby

Longfield

B260

ROCHESTER

1

A   **B**   **C**   **D**

JUNCTIONS
1–4

JUNCTION
–2–

EXIT SIGNS

Travelling clockwise   A2   Rochester
Dover (M2)
London

Travelling anticlockwise   A2   London SE
Rochester

Catford   Casa Cominetti

129 Rushey Green. 01-697 2314 ● Map 5C2. Take A2 (London SE) and follow signs for Eltham (A210). At first roundabout join the A205 South Circular Road. Follow one-way system around Catford towards Lewisham. Restaurant is on right after the Town Hall. ● Lunch 12–2.30. Dinner 7–10.30 ● About £35 for two ● *Credit* Access, Amex, Diners, Visa ● Closed Sun, Mon, Bank Holidays, August & 3 days Christmas

Separate trolleys bearing antipasti, fresh fish and shellfish, as well as sweets, make a colourful and appetising display at this bright, long-established Italian restaurant. The menu offers a wide choice of well-prepared favourites, ranging from tasty minestrone, stracciatella, cannelloni and risotto to calf's liver with sage and saltimbocca alla romana – with seasonal additions too. Fish includes fried scampi, grilled trout and skate, and for red meat eaters there is fillet steak with a tomato, mushroom and white wine sauce or lamb cutlets with a rosemary sauce. Sweets are simple but good, including fresh gâteaux and Italian ice-creams. ℮

Greenwich   Le Premier Cru

328 Creek Road. 01-858 9222 ● Map 5D1.
Take A2 (London SE). Follow signs for
Blackheath and then for Greenwich town
centre. From Greenwich High Road
(A206), follow signs for Deptford. Turn left
off High Rd into Creek Road. Restaurant is
on left ● Lunch 12–3. Dinner 7–11 ● Set L
£5·25. About £19 for two ● *Credit* Access,
Amex, Diners, Visa ● Closed L Sat, D Sun,
all Mon (except Bank Holidays), Tues after
Bank Holiday Mons, 25 December–1
January

Owner–chef Brian Bealing serves robust portions of good,
unpretentious food at this pleasant, informal little restaurant
only a stone's throw from the Cutty Sark. Menu is largely
French in style, featuring a number of familiar dishes like sole
bonne femme, coq au vin and veal cordon bleu. Vegetables
arrive without ceremony on the same plate as the main
course. Interesting egg dishes include poached eggs served
in a white wine sauce with fried onion rings and egg in curried
mayonnaise with prawns and cucumber. ☺

Greenwich   Spread Eagle

2 Stockwell Street. 01-853 2333 ● Map
5D1. Take A2 (London SE), follow signs for
Blackheath and then for Greenwich town
centre. From Greenwich High Road
(A206), turn right into Stockwell Street
after the Town Hall. Restaurant is on right
● Lunch 12–2.30. Dinner 6.30–10.30 ● Set
L £9·75. Set D £13·50. About £40 for two ●
Credit Access, Amex, Diners, Visa ●
Closed L Sat, all Sun & 4 days Christmas

This cosy, Victorian-style restaurant was once a busy
coaching inn with theatrical connections, which now continue
with the Greenwich Theatre opposite. Monthly changes bring
a seasonal flavour to the menu and dishes are prepared with
real skill and enthusiasm. Starters might include scallops with
a delicate saffron and tomato sauce or a sweetbread and
quail terrine with cherry vinaigrette and roasted pine kernels.
To follow there might be fillet of sole stuffed with fish and
tarragon mouse served in a prawn sauce or – for vegetarians
– spinach parcels of three different puréed vegetables coated
with a cheese sauce. Cheerful service. ☺

HOTEL

Shorne — Inn on the Lake

62%
£E

Near Gravesend, Kent. Shorne (047 482) 3333 ● Map 5H2. Follow signs for Gravesend and Rochester. The hotel is signposted off A2 just beyond the exit for Gravesend East ● Bedrooms 78. En suite 78. With phone 78. With TV 78 ● Confirm by 6 ● *Credit* Access, Amex, Diners, Visa

This low-rise modern hotel enjoys a delightful setting of 12 acres of grounds, complete with twin lakes, waterfalls – and resident ducks! Staff offer a particularly cordial welcome, and relaxing is easy in the cheerful public areas. Bedrooms are furnished in functional modern style and offer direct-dial phones, remote-control TVs, trouser presses, hairdryers, tea-makers and fresh fruit. Best rooms have pretty views over the lakes while those at the front are shielded from traffic noise by excellent double glazing. Practical, fully-tiled private bathrooms throughout. No dogs. *Amenities* garden, coarse fishing, dinner dance (Sat), 24-hour lounge service.

JUNCTION
–3–

EXIT SIGNS

Travelling clockwise	M20	Maidstone Folkestone Dover
	A20	London Swanley
Travelling anticlockwise	A20	London
	M20	Maidstone
	B2173	Swanley

Chislehurst — Mrs Bridges' Kitchen

49 Chislehurst Road, Kent. 01-467 2150 ●
Map 5D2. Take A20 and turn left onto
A222 to Chislehurst. This becomes
Chislehurst Road. Café is on right, close to
railway station ● Open 8am–2pm (Sat from
9). Closed Sun, Bank Holidays & 10 days
Christmas ● *Credit* Access, Visa

Colourful hanging lanterns, fin-de-siècle posters and wood-panelled walls give a warm and cheerful feel to this honest and unpretentious little café-diner. Emphasis is on simple, satisfying dishes based on good fresh produce. Hearty farmhouse breakfasts fuel early birds (and are available throughout the day) while lunchtime brings home-made soups, omelettes, mixed grills and bumper toasted sandwiches, plus salads, ploughman's and a caveman's lunch with home-cooked gammon. Chicken casserole served in a tomato sauce is another popular item. Puddings include a delicious treacle tart. No dogs. *Typical prices*: Chicken casserole £1·90 Mixed grill £2·45. WC

Fawkham — Brandshatch Place

68%
£C

Kent. Ash Green (0474) 872239 ● Map
5G3. Follow signs for Maidstone, take A20
(not M20) into West Kingsdown. Turn left
into Fawkham Road (by Portobollo Inn);
turn first right and then second right again.
Hotel is on right ● Bedrooms 26. En suite
26. With phone 26. With TV 26 ● Confirm
by arrangement ● *Credit* Access, Amex,
Diners, Visa

Mel Taylor and her team contribute greatly to the pleasure of a stay in this Georgian country mansion. The lounge, library-bar and conservatory are all delightfully relaxing, and bedrooms are comfortably appointed in traditional style with modern touches like smart duvets (blankets available as an alternative). Though attractively set in 12 acres of gardens and grounds, the hotel is close to the M20 and benefits from double glazing on its exposed flank. No dogs. *Amenities* garden, sauna, indoor swimming pool, tennis, squash, solarium, clay-pigeon shooting, badminton, laundry service, snooker, gymnasium, children's play area, coffee shop (10am–11pm).

Junction 3

Fawkham Brandshatch Place Restaurant

Kent. Ash Green (0474) 872239 ● Map
5G3. See hotel entry for directions ● Lunch
12–2.30. Dinner 7–9.30 ● About £48 for
two ● *Credit* Access, Amex, Diners, Visa ●
Closed L Sat, all Sun & 25 December–4
January

Light textures, fine flavours and first-class presentation mark
Colin Liddy's style but he is by no means a slave to modern
trends. He can startle with the unusual combination of Parma
ham with a pineapple and black pepper sorbet or reassure
with a creamy, gently-seasoned broccoli soup. Main courses
might be as deliciously simple as cutlets of tender English
lamb served with a minted butter sauce or as elaborate as
poached fillets of sole filled with shredded crabmeat and
accompanied by a lobster sauce. Al dente vegetables.
Vegetarian menu and nice sweets. Good list of clarets and
burgundies. ♀ *WELL-CHOSEN* house wine

JUNCTION
–4–

EXIT SIGNS

Travelling clockwise	A21 Bromley
	A224 Orpington
Travelling anticlockwise	A21 Bromley
	A224 Orpington

Bromley	Bromley Court Hotel

67%
£D

Bromley Hill, Kent. 01-464 5011 ● Map
5C3. Take A21 through Bromley centre,
following signs for Lewisham & Downham.
Hotel is on left just outside town centre ●
Bedrooms 130. En suite 130. With phone
130. With TV 130 ● Confirm by 6 ● *Credit*
Access, Amex, Diners, Visa

A sweeping drive leads to this 19th-century mansion with modern extensions. Up-to-date accommodation is smart and neatly fitted: all bedrooms have direct-dial phones, colour TVs and tea-makers. Among the public rooms are a spacious foyer-lounge with modern, low-slung sofas and a handsome cocktail bar with stately columns, chandelier, marble fireplace and delightful views of the garden. This is obviously tended with great care and devotion and features a pretty rose-trellised walkway. *Amenities* garden, putting, golf practice net, dinner dance (Sat), coffee shop (10.30am–10.30pm), 24-hour lounge service, laundry service.

Bromley	Capisano's

7 Simpsons Road, Kent. 01-464 8036 ●
Map 5C3. Take A21 into Bromley. Turn left
at the bottom of Mason's Hill into
Westmoreland Road. Then take first right
turn. Restaurant is on right ● Lunch 12–
2.30. Dinner 7–11 ● Set L £7·50. About £28
for two ● *Credit* Access, Amex, Visa ●
Closed Sun, Mon, Bank Holidays except
Good Friday & 3 weeks August–
September

Chianti bottles and waiters dressed in red shirts set the tone of this popular Italian restaurant, situated next to a busy shopping precinct. The menu offers a good range of old favourites – plenty of seafood antipasti, hearty soups like minestrone or pasta and bean, all the usual pastas, veal or stuffed chicken escalopes in a number of sauces, plus grilled fish, calf's liver and steak. Sweets come mainly from the trolley, although there are ices and a nice zabaglione. Cooking is reliably good and Capisano's deserves its faithful following.
Ⓔ

Bromley   Hollywood Bowl

5 Market Parade, Kent. 01-460 2346 ●
Map 5C3. Take A21 into Bromley. Follow
one-way system round. Turn first left at the
roundabout by the Town Hall and then
second left. Restaurant is on right ● Open
noon–2.45 & 6–11.15 (Fri & Sat till 11.45,
Sun till 11). Closed Sun lunch & Bank
Holidays (except Good Fri)

Red check tablecloths and a splendid collection of old enamel
advertising signs around the walls contribute to the lively,
informal atmosphere of this American-style restaurant. Ham-
burgers are the things to order, cooked how you like and
served in a toasted bun with toppings like chilli or melted
cheese. Alternative main dishes include lamb cutlets, herb-
fried chicken, lasagne and quiche. Salads and bumper
sandwiches are also available. To follow, there are puddings
like cheesecake and chocolate fudge cake – alas, not home-
made. Service is swift and friendly. No dogs. *Typical prices*:
Chilli burger £3·95 Baked Brie with almonds £1·25. WC

Bromley   Peking Diner

71 Burnt Ash Lane, Kent. 01-464 7911 ●
Map 5C3. Take A21 into Bromley. Follow
one-way system round. Turn left by the
Post Office into West Street. Follow signs
for Grove Park. Restaurant is on right ●
Lunch 12–2.30. Dinner 6.30–12 ● Set D
from £7. About £30 for two ● *Credit*
Access, Amex, Diners, Visa ● Closed Sun
& Bank Holidays

Mainly Pekinese dishes are on offer at this smart modern
Chinese restaurant, where stylish wicker chairs, fresh flowers
and sparkling white tablecloths create an impression of cool
elegance. Working your way through the vast and quaintly-
styled menu can take time but, having ordered, you can be
confident that an excellent meal is on its way. Fried seaweed
with shredded scallops and sesame toast with shrimps make
appetising starters, and to follow there's delicious aromatic
crispy duck with pancakes as well as a wide selection of
seafood dishes like baked crab with ginger, steamed bass or
sweet and sour prawns. Service is helpful.

Keston   Giannino's

6 Commonside, near Bromley, Kent.
Farnborough (0689) 56410 ● Map 5D3.
Follow signs for Bromley (A21). Turn off
for Croydon (A232) and follow for one mile.
Turn left into Commonside. Restaurant is
on left ● Lunch 12–2.30. Dinner 7–10 ● Set
L £9·25. About £40 for two ● *Credit*
Access, Amex, Diners, Visa ● Closed Sun,
Mon, August & 24 December–3 January

Standards remain high at this cheerful Italian restaurant, a
rustic L-shaped room with a covered terrace for warm-
weather eating. Proprietor Giannino Artini is welcoming and
attentive and service is good-humoured and informal. There's
nothing fancy about the food, yet it is prepared with such care
and skill, using only the very best ingredients, that familiar
dishes are raised to new heights. Sauces are superb, from
the tasty clam sauce served with pasta – al dente, of course –
to the finely-flavoured Marsala sauce that accompanies veal
escalopes of melting tenderness. Sweets are as delicious as
they look. Booking advisable.

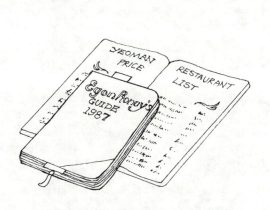

Changes in data may occur in
establishments after the Guide goes
to press. Prices should be taken
as indications rather than firm quotes.

JUNCTIONS
5–6

JUNCTION
–5–

EXIT SIGNS

Travelling clockwise	A21	Sevenoaks Hastings
Travelling anticlockwise	M26 (M20)	Maidstone Folkestone Dover
	A21	Sevenoaks Hastings

Hadlow **La Crémaillère**

The Square, near Tonbridge, Kent. Hadlow (0732) 851489 ● Map 6H2. Take A21 towards Hastings. Follow signs for B245 into Tonbridge. Then take A26 (Maidstone) into Hadlow. Restaurant is on right in village centre ● Lunch 12.30–1.30. Dinner 8–9 ● Set L & D £10·50. About £33 for two ● *Credit* Access, Amex, Diners, Visa ● Closed L Sat, all Sun, Bank Holidays, 1 week January, also 3 other weeks annually

An understandably popular restaurant, where Brittany-born Michel Maillard cooks with assured skill. In winter you can dine by candlelight beside an open fire in the 200-year-old dining room, while in summer you might prefer to lunch in the light and airy conservatory with its delightful trailing vines. Good value set menus offer starters like salmon feuilleté with hollandaise sauce or pâté de campagne to precede saffron-poached monkfish or a highly enjoyable duck casserole with turnips. Crisp fresh vegetables are served in burnished copper pots and there are some nice desserts. Charming service. ♀ *WELL-CHOSEN* house wine.

RESTAURANT

51

PUB

Hildenborough   Gate Inn

(Food)

Rings Hill, Kent. Hildenborough (0732)
832103 ● Map 6G3. Take A21 (Hastings).
Follow signs for North Tonbridge (B245)
and then for Hildenborough station ● Last
bar food 10pm ● *Credit* Amex, Visa ●
Brewery Whitbread. *Beers* Fremlins Bitter;
Flowers Original; Guinness; Heineken;
Stella Artois; cider

Seafood's the name of the game at this characterful pub next
to the station. Nice Victorian touches include real gas lighting,
a couple of old beer engines and pew seating. Daily deliveries
from Billingsgate bring red mullet, conger eel and John Dory
for the excellent fish soup, and you'll also find crab and
lobster, mussels and oysters, sole and salmon on the menu.
The occasional meaty special appears at lunchtime and puds
might include hazelnut and passion fruit roulade with locally
made double cream. Garden. *Typical prices:* Salmon en
croûte £7 Avocado vinaigrette £1·25. No bar food Sun or
Bank Hol Mons. ☻

PUB

Ide Hill   Cock Inn

(Food)

Near Sevenoaks, Kent. Ide Hill (073 275)
310 ● Map 6F2. Follow signs for
Sevenoaks (A21) and then take A25
(Westerham). Turn left at traffic lights by
White Horse in Sundridge. Pub is on left
opposite church ● Last bar food 8.30pm ●
Brewery Friary Meux. *Beers* Friary Meux
Traditional Bitter; Ind Coope Burton Ale;
Guinness; Skol; cider

Bring a hearty appetite along to this friendly old pub on the
village green. Bob and Jackie Arnett's wholesome snacks
served in the two beamed bars aren't for faint hearts: choose
from moist, chunky pâté and hot salt beef, ploughman's with
horseradish, salads, herby sausages locally made and steaks.
Seafood specials like grilled Dover sole are worth looking out
for: the landlord's brother runs a trawler off the South Coast
and supplies all the fish direct. Simple puds. Sandwiches only
Sun lunchtime. Terrace. *Typical prices:* Salt beef ploughman's
£1·60 Sirloin with chips & salad £6. No bar food Sun eve. ☻

Ightham   Town House

Near Sevenoaks, Kent. Borough Green
(0732) 884578 ● Map 6G1. Follow signs for
Sevenoaks (A21), then for Maidstone via
Seal on A25. Turn right after Ightham by-
pass onto A227 which leads directly to
village centre. Restaurant is on right ●
Dinner only 7–9.30 ● Set D from £19·50.
About £50 for two ● *Credit* Access, Amex,
Diners, Visa ● Closed Sun, Mon, 2 weeks
Easter, 2 weeks August–September & 2
weeks Christmas

Graham Poole's superb cooking is matched by an equally
impressive setting – the lofty timbered hall of a handsome old
house. Beautifully presented starters range from a fresh,
moist chicken-liver mousse studded with prunes, wrapped in
puff pastry and served with a rich Sauternes sauce, to a tasty
duckling terrine accompanied by blackcurrant coulis. Main
courses feature such delights as halibut studded with truffles
and served with a raspberry vinegar sauce or medallions of
venison with a rum and honey sauce. Masterful desserts
include chilled peppermint or caramel mousses, mille-feuilles
and a wickedly rich nesselrode pudding. ♀ *WELL-CHOSEN*
house wine.

Penshurst   Fir Tree House Tea Rooms

Near Tonbridge, Kent. Penshurst (0892)
870382 ● Map 6F3. Take A21 towards
Hastings and follow signs (B2027 and
B2110) into Penshurst ● Open 3–6. Closed
Mon in season (except Bank Holidays
when closed Tues), Mon–Fri January–
Easter & all November & December

Approaching the centre of the village you can see the Tudor
windows of the tea rooms right next door to the village hall.
Inside, customers are seated on Victorian pews made of pitch
pine to enjoy Caroline Fuller-Rowell's delicious teas: lovely
light scones with whipped cream and home-made jam, plus
other freshly-baked goodies like coffee and walnut sponge,
chocolate cake and nut-studded tea bread. The building is
overlooked by fir trees, and there's a pretty garden at the
back for use on fine summer afternoons. Unlicensed. No
smoking. *Typical prices:* Tea & scones £1·50 Strawberry tea
£2·20. 🐾

RESTAURANT

Sevenoaks — Le Chantecler

43 High Street, Kent. Sevenoaks (0732)
454662 ● Map 6F1. Follow signs for
Sevenoaks (A21, A25 & A2028). Turn right
off A2028 into High Street (signposted
Tonbridge). Restaurant is on right ● Lunch
12.30–2. Dinner 7.30–10 ● Set L £7·50. Set
D Tues–Thurs £10·50. About £38 for two ●
Credit Access, Amex, Diners, Visa ●
Closed L Sat, all Sun & Mon & Bank
Holidays

Gill Ginzler is the talented chef at this attractive restaurant in a 17th-century building with charming walled garden. Husband Alan welcomes and assists at the front of the house, directing a smart young team who provide excellent service. The familiar blends with the original on a menu that could include confit de canard (presented cold as a starter), fish of the day and calf's kidneys served deliciously pink with a subtle mustard sauce. Spot-on vegetables. Admirable sweet trolley might feature a beautifully rich chocolate log, made with the best Belgian chocolate. French regional set menu Tuesday–Thursday evenings. ☺

HOTEL

Tonbridge — Rose & Crown Hotel

60%
£D

125 High Street, Kent. Tonbridge (0732)
357966 ● Map 6G3. Follow signs for
Hastings (A21) and then for North
Tonbridge (B245). This leads into High
Street. Hotel is on left ● Bedrooms 51. En
suite 51. With phone 51. With TV 51 ●
Confirm by 6 ● *Credit* Access, Amex,
Diners, Visa

The distinctive blue- and red-brick facade of this former coaching inn dates back to the 18th century. Inside, black beams and Jacobean panelling bear testament to an older building. The cosy little lounge has been stylishly refurbished, and there are several attractive function rooms with a nice period feel to them. Bedrooms vary from charming and traditional (in the original building) to practical and modern (in two wings). Many have been recently redecorated; all are well equipped with remote-control TVs, direct-dial phones and tea-makers. Good private bathrooms throughout. *Amenities* garden, solarium, 24-hour lounge service.

Westerham   Henry Wilkinson

26 Market Square, Kent. Westerham
(0959) 64245 ● Map 6E2. Take A21
(Sevenoaks) and follow signs for
Westerham. Wine bar is in the centre of
town on right opposite the obelisk ● Open
noon–2.30 & 7–10.30 (Fri–Sat till 11.30).
Closed Mon eve, all Sun, Good Fri & 25 &
26 December ● *Credit* Access, Amex,
Diners, Visa

Wholesome, home-made food is a major attraction at this
town-centre wine bar, where all the tables are ready laid for
eating. If it wasn't for the counter service, the place would
appear more like a bistro than a wine bar. Menu varies from
lunchtime to evening, although staples like omelettes, grills
and salads are available at both sessions. Steak sandwiches
and jacket potatoes are typical lunchtime snacks, while in the
evening there are hot meat dishes like beef chasseur and
Swiss veal. Sweet and savoury endings. *Typical prices:* Beef
chasseur £4·85 Taramasalata £2·05. No dogs. ☺

JUNCTION
–6–

EXIT SIGNS

Travelling clockwise	A22 East Grinstead Caterham Redhill
Travelling anticlockwise	A22 Caterham East Grinstead Westerham Godstone

PUB

Bletchingley   Whyte Hart

(B&B)
£E

High Street, Surrey. Godstone (0883) 843231 ● Map 6C2. Take A22 to Godstone and follow signs for Redhill (A25) for approximately 1½ miles ● Bedrooms 9. With bath/shower 4. With TV none. Check-in restricted ● *Credit* Access, Amex, Diners, Visa ● *Brewery* Allied. *Beers* Ind Coope Burton Ale; Friary Meux Bitter; John Bull Bitter; Guinness; Castlemaine 4X; Skol; cider

Smartly and freshly painted in black and white, this 600-year-old inn takes pride of place in the main street. Inside, everything is delightfully mellow, from the entrance hall with well-worn brick floor to the bar with huge old inglenook fireplace, burnished copper and brass and venerable furniture polished by age to a fine patina. Spick-and-span little bedroooms have pretty matching curtains and bedcovers; four simply fitted rooms have en suite facilities, whereas traditionally furnished rooms in the oldest part of the building share two public bathrooms. There's a tiny TV lounge. Garden. No dogs in rooms.

RESTAURANT

East Grinstead   Evergreen

192 London Road, West Sussex. East Grinstead (0342) 22078 ● Map 6D4. Take A22 to East Grinstead. Restaurant is on right before town centre ● Lunch 12–2. Dinner 5.30–11.30, Fri & Sat 5.30–12, Sun 6–11.30 ● Set L & D from £9·50. About £25 for two ● *Credit* Access, Amex, Diners, Visa ● Closed L Sun & all 25 & 26 December

Owner Mr Lin applies his culinary skills to a wide range of dishes in this stylish Chinese restaurant. Favourites from Peking like aromatic crispy duck with pancakes are his forte, and there are also plenty of good things from other regions (Canton, Szechuan). Specials could include delights like sea bass or quick-fried scallops with ginger and spring onion. The dried scallops, combined with crisp seaweed, are also surprisingly good. Nice crunchy vegetables, all quick-fried to perfection. Excellent rice, whether plain or 'special' (fried with egg and fresh prawn). Faultless service, though typically reserved. ♀ *WELL-CHOSEN* house wine.

East Grinstead — Felbridge Hotel

65%
£D/E

London Road, West Sussex. East Grinstead (0342) 26992 ● Map 6D4. Take A22 (East Grinstead). Hotel is on left just beyond Felbridge ● Bedrooms 49. En suite 49. With phone 49. With TV 49 ● Confirm by arrangement ● *Credit* Access, Amex, Diners, Visa

Standing in extensive, well-kept gardens, this busy hotel offers impressive leisure facilities. The main bar, with beams and settles, is agreeably traditional; a newer, pub-style bar plies a busy trade in lunchtime snacks. Business functions are well catered for, with a good choice of meeting rooms. Best bedrooms are those in the Bahama wing, with bright, contemporary decor and up-to-the-minute bathrooms; many have private balconies. Other rooms are more basic, but all are clean and carefully maintained. No dogs. *Amenities* garden, sauna, indoor & outdoor swimming pools, solarium, whirlpool bath, gymnasiums, snooker, beauty salon.

Edenbridge — Buffin's Restaurant

95 High Street, Kent. Edenbridge (0732) 863938 ● Map 6E3. Follow signs for Westerham (A22 & A25). Turn right at Limpsfield Common onto B269 and follow signs for Edenbridge. Restaurant is on the left by the bridge ● Open 10–2, also 7.30–9 (Thurs & Fri) & 7.30–10 (Sat). Closed Sun, Mon, 1 January & 25 & 26 December ● *Credit* Access, Amex, Diners, Visa

Located on the main street, this black-beamed restaurant has a warm, homely feel. In the morning you can tuck into a traditional English breakfast or enjoy a teacake, a Danish pastry or Black Forest gâteau. Omelettes are also available, and from noon there are main courses such as grilled plaice, lamb cutlets, a salad or the day's roast. Simple starters like soup of the day or fruit juice, and desserts chosen from the trolley. More elaborate evening meals and traditional Sunday lunch. Half-portions available. No dogs. *Typical prices:* Escalope of veal £2·50 Banana & rum gâteau 90p. ◔

Kenley   Wattenden Arms

(Food)

Old Lodge Lane, Surrey. 01-660 8638 ●
Map 6C1. Take A22 to Caterham. Turn left
onto B2030 for Caterham-on-the-Hill.
Follow signs for Kenley aerodrome. Turn
left immediately after aerodrome. Pub is
on left ● Last bar food 9pm ● *Brewery*
Charrington. *Beers* Bass Bitter,
Charrington IPA; Fuller's ESB (winter
only); Stones Bitter; Guinness; Tennents
Extra; cider

Ron and Joan Coulston offer a warm welcome and tasty bar
food at this charming old pub – one of the two oldest buildings
in the village. An aircraft propeller adorning the bar recalls a
more recent era when the pub became an RAF officers' mess
during World War II. There's a tempting display of cold meats,
seafood and salad, or you can order hot dishes like soup,
chicken curry, fried plaice or ham, egg and chips. Nice
traditional desserts like spotted dick and bread and butter
pudding. Sandwiches only on Sun. Garden. *Typical prices:*
Prawn curry £3 Beef salad £3. ◔

Limpsfield   Limpsfield Brasserie

High Street, Surrey. Oxted (088 33) 7385 ●
Map 6E2. Take A22, then A25 through
Oxted and follow signs for Warlingham
(B269). Restaurant is on right ● Open 11–3
& 6–11. Closed lunch Mon & Sat, all Sun, 1
January, Good Fri & 25 & 26 December ●
Credit Access, Visa

The bar snacks have really caught on at the Old Lodge, and
as a result the bar has acquired not only a separate name and
entrance but also its very own chef. The menu is straightforward, with starters like pâté, lasagne or outstanding individual
quiche lorraine and main dishes such as fish pie, steak and
kidney pie or chicken kebabs served with potatoes and salad.
Desserts are especially good, whether traditional hot puds
like apple crumble or chilled desserts like fresh strawberry
cheesecake with strawberry coulis. No dogs. *Typical prices:*
Steak & kidney pie £4·50 Prawn & pineapple salad £2·50. ◔
WC

Limpsfield   Old Lodge

High Street, Surrey. Oxted (088 33) 2996 ●
Map 6E2. See previous entry for directions
● Lunch 12.30–2. Dinner 7.30–9 ● Set L
from £14, Sun £14·50. Set D from £14.
About £50 for two ● *Credit* Access, Amex,
Diners, Visa ● Closed L Sat, D Sun, all
Mon, 1st 2 weeks January & Good Friday

There's a choice of two set menus at this sophisticated French restaurant – also a 'menu exceptionnel' that consists of six surprise courses. All three menus are interesting and imaginative and, at its best, the food is carefully cooked and attractively presented. Typical of the starters is a crisp puff pastry case filled with fresh oyster mushrooms and asparagus tips served on a pale red basil-flavoured sauce. Liqueurs are frequently used to flavour sauces and desserts, as in quails with Grand Marnier and orange sauce, but sometimes the flavour of the liqueur is rather elusive. Nice crisp vegetables. Service professional and attentive. ☺

South Godstone   La Bonne Auberge

Tilburston Hill, Surrey. South Godstone
(0342) 892318 ● Map 6D3. Take A22
through Godstone. Take right-hand fork at
Bell Inn. Restaurant is 2 miles down on
right ● Lunch 12–2. Dinner 7–10 ● Set L
£13·50 & £16·50. Set D from £14·25. About
£50 for two ● *Credit* Access, Amex, Visa ●
Closed D Sun, all Mon, L Sat occasionally
& D 26–30 December

Food is taken very seriously at this attractive country-house restaurant, noted for its excellent French cooking and now celebrating its silver jubilee. Jean-Pierre Bonnet's sure skills are matched by outstandingly attentive service. No short cuts are taken here and only the finest raw materials are used. Salad of artichoke heart, grapes, walnut and quail, mussels and spinach mille-feuille, caul-wrapped lamb cutlets with a minced vegetable stuffing and rich Madeira sauce and sirloin steak with morels are typical delights. Noteworthy vegetables and a nice sweet selection. Good-value clarets and Beaujolais crus. ☺ ♀ *WELL-CHOSEN* house wine.

JUNCTIONS
7–8

JUNCTION
–7–

EXIT SIGNS

Travelling clockwise	M23	Gatwick Crawley Brighton Croydon
Travelling anticlockwise	M23	Gatwick East Grinstead Brighton Croydon

---

Copthorne	Copthorne Hotel

£C 71%

Near Crawley, West Sussex. Copthorne (0342) 714971 ●
Map 7C8. Take M23 (Brighton) to junction 10. Then take A264 towards East Grinstead. Hotel is on right and signposted ● Bedrooms

223. En suite 223. With phone 223. With TV 223 ● Confirm by 6 ● *Credit* Access, Amex, Diners, Visa

This executive-oriented hotel is fronted by a converted 16th-century farmhouse. The beamed bar retains much of the old-world atmosphere of the original house, while modern public areas include well-equipped conference rooms and a chic, tile-floored garden room that overlooks an ornamental water garden. Bedrooms provide every modern comfort and convenience. The whole place is beautifully maintained. *Amenities* garden, sauna, solarium, gymnasium, squash, 24-hour lounge service, hairdressing, kiosk, grill room (5.30am–11pm), croquet, transport to airport, ceefax, laundry service.

HOTEL

Copthorne   Copthorne Hotel Restaurant

Near Crawley, West Sussex. Copthorne
(0342) 714971 ● Map 7C8. See hotel entry
for directions. ● Lunch 12.30–2.30 Dinner
7.30–10 ● Set L £12·50 Set D £17·50 About
£50 for two ● *Credit* Access, Amex,
Diners, Visa ● Closed L Sat, all Sun, 1 day
Easter & 3 days Christmas

The menu in this roomy, comfortable restaurant is largely
French inspired. There are few surprises but the cooking is
generally sound. Dishes span button mushrooms in a cream
and brandy sauce layered in puff pastry, cider-poached skate
in an apple, tomato and basil sauce, tournedos Roquefort
and veal escalope ruine de mère (a gin-based sauce!)
garnished with braised endive. Also simpler grills and roasts.
Vegetables are variable. Conventional sweet trolley offers an
appetizing choice, including a very acceptable dark and
smooth-textured chocolate mousse. Well-drilled though
rather formal service. Wines very pricey.⊘

Croydon   Chalet Suisse

32 Selsdon Road, Surrey. 01-688 8777 ●
Map 7C3. Take M23 and follow signs to
Croydon via Purley (A23 & A235). Turn
right into Selsdon Road about 2 miles
beyond Purley ● Lunch 12–2.30. Dinner 7–
12, Sat 6–12 ● Set L from £6·90. Set D
from £13·50. About £40 for two ● *Credit*
Access, Amex, Visa ● Closed L Sat, all
Sun, 1 January & 27 December

Swiss specialities, notably charcuterie and fondues, are a
popular feature at this friendly chalet-style restaurant. New
chef-patron André Massena comes from Nice and although
he intends keeping the Swiss side of the menu, his wide-
ranging repertoire shows a strong modern French influence.
Nouvelle-style dishes he has introduced include lightly
sautéed chicken livers served in an airy case of flaky pastry
with a finely-flavoured port wine sauce, tender poussin in a
refreshing orange sauce, and a tasty monkfish terrine. Sauces
are a strong point, vegetables are excellent and there are
some mouthwatering desserts. Impeccable service. ⊘
♀ *WELL-CHOSEN* house wine.

Croydon   Hockneys

98 High Street, Surrey. 01-688 2899 ● Map
7C3. Take M23 then A23 and A235 into
Croydon. Restaurant is on left of High
Street just before flyover ● Open noon–
10.30. Closed Sun, Mon, Bank Holidays, 2
weeks August & 2 weeks Christmas ●
Credit Access, Amex, Diners, Visa

Hockney etchings and other contemporary prints line the
walls of this friendly vegetarian restaurant run by Buddhists.
There's counter service till 5.30, then table service and slightly
higher prices. The wide-ranging menu includes starters such
as houmus and gazpacho; quiches, falafel and vegeburgers;
salads; and main dishes like spinach lasagne and gado gado.
Lots of tempting cakes and sweets, including carrot cake and
a superb rum and raisin parfait. Book for dinner. Unlicensed,
so bring your own wine (£1.35 corkage per bottle). No
smoking. No dogs. *Typical prices:* Spicy mushroom soup £1
(£1·55 eve) Lasagne £3·10 (£3·75 eve). ⊘ WC

Croydon   Holiday Inn

£C 71%

7 Altyre Road, Surrey. 01-680
9200 ● Map 7C3. Take M23,
then A23 and A235 into
Croydon. Follow signs for
East Croydon Railway
Station. Take 3rd exit off
roundabout after station.

Hotel is on right ● Bedrooms 214. En suite 214. With phone
214. With TV 214 ● Confirm by 6 ● *Credit* Access, Amex,
Diners, Visa

Excellent accommodation and fine facilities for business and
leisure combine in this modern red-brick hotel. The spacious
mirrored and marble-floored foyer-lounge has comfortable
sitting areas. Pastel prints and wicker furniture set the style
in the coffee shop, and the brick-walled bar has an Edwardian
gaslight theme. Smart, good-sized bedrooms are individually
air conditioned and have well-equipped bathrooms. Extra
accessories in executive rooms and suites. *Amenities* indoor
swimming pool, patio, keep-fit equipment, sauna, solarium,
whirlpool bath, squash, coffee shop (6am–11pm), kiosk, in-
house movies, baby listening, laundry service.

Croydon   Munbhave

305 London Road, West Croydon, Surrey.
01-689 6331 ● Map 7C3. Take M23 then
A23 and A235 into Croydon. Restaurant is
on the left beyond West Croydon Station ●
Open 6pm–11pm (Sat till midnight). Closed
Mon, 1 January, 25 & 26 December & 2
weeks summer ● *Credit* Access, Visa

This friendly family-run restaurant specialises in the Gujarati
style of Indian vegetarian cooking. Judicious spicing en-
hances good fresh flavours through a range that includes
samosas, bhajias, puris, masala dhosa (pancake filled with
mixed vegetables and served with a yoghurt and spice sauce,
green chutney and coconut) and sweet or salted lassi. Whole
stuffed aubergine is a speciality, and thalis (set meals) provide
a well-balanced selection of dishes. Jovial Kesh Tank,
assisted by other members of the family, attends to the
customers while his wife runs the kitchen. No dogs. *Typical
prices:* Stuffed aubergine £3·85 Masala dhosa £3·95. WC

Croydon   Selsdon Park Hotel

69%
£B/C

Addington Road, Sanderstead, Surrey. 01-
657 8811 ● Map 7C3. Take M23
(Croydon), then A23 to Purley. Turn right in
Purley onto Godstone Road (A22), then left
onto A2022 towards Selsdon. Hotel is this
side of Selsdon ● Bedrooms 150. En suite
150. With phone 150. With TV 150 ●
Confirm by arrangement ● *Credit* Access,
Amex, Diners, Visa

An impressive leisure complex and a peaceful location are
among the attractions of this stylish hotel, owned and run by
the Sanderson family. The house itself has a long history,
recalled by the handsome moulded ceilings and a family tree
in stained glass. Bedrooms, which are kept spick-and-span
by continuous refurbishment, vary widely in size; all offer
wall-safes and remote-control TV. *Amenities* garden, golf
course, croquet, riding, children's playground, indoor and
outdoor swimming pools, tennis, squash, keep-fit equipment,
sauna, solarium, whirlpool bath, billiards, snooker, dinner
dance (Sat), 24-hour lounge service, laundry service, helipad.

RESTAURANT

Croydon   Tung Kum

205 High Street, Surrey. 01-688 0748 ●
Map 7C3. Take M23 then A23 and A235
into Croydon. Restaurant is on right of
High Street before the flyover ● Lunch 12–
2.30. Dinner 5–11.15. Sat & Sun noon–
11.15 ● About £30 for two ● *Credit*
Access, Amex, Diners, Visa ● Closed Bank
Holidays

Among the bright lights of Croydon is a bold yellow neon sign indicating the whereabouts of this busy Chinese restaurant. Inside there's nothing sophisticated about the decor (plastic-covered chairs and a stylised Chinese landscape along one wall) but the food, though simple and unambitious, is tasty and well-prepared. The menu concentrates mainly on Cantonese dishes. There's plenty of choice, from wun tun soup and special egg roll with meat and vegetable filling to crispy duck with sweet and sour sauce, crab and beef with bamboo shoots. Nicely crunchy, mixed vegetables include baby sweetcorn and straw mushrooms.

PUB

Croydon   Windsor Castle

(B&B)
£E

415 Brighton Road, Surrey. 01-680 4559 ●
Map 7C3. Take M23 then A23 and A235
into Croydon. Pub is on right beyond Royal
Oak Centre. ● Bedrooms 30. With bath/
shower 30. With TV 30. Check-in all day ●
Credit Access, Amex, Diners, Visa ●
Brewery Bass. *Beers* Bass Bitter,
Charrington IPA; Stones Bitter; Toby
Bitter; Guinness; Carling Black Label;
Pilsner; Tennent's Extra

This former coaching inn on the busy Brighton Road has provided overnight accommodation for centuries, but the modern purpose-built block of bedrooms located behind the main building was completed only five years ago. Rooms are comfortably furnished, with good-quality carpets and practical fitted units. They're equipped with every modern facility, from tea-makers and trouser presses to radio-alarms and remote-control TVs. Neat, fully-tiled bathrooms have heated towel rails and plenty of towels. There are three bars, including the Edwardian-style Windsor Bar designated for residents and a lively public bar. Terrace. No dogs in rooms.

Croydon — Wine Vaults

122 North End, Surrey. 01-680 2419 ● Map
7C3. Take M23 then A23 and A235 into
Croydon. Wine bar is on right, just before
West Croydon Station. ● Open 11.30–3 &
5.30–10.30 (Fri & Sat till 11). Closed Sun &
Bank Holidays ● *Credit* Access, Amex,
Diners, Visa

Atmospheric cellar wine bar with sawdust, candles and huge casks of port and sherry on display. The partitioned alcoves are perfect for a discreet rendezvous or private business chat. Either here or at the bar you can nibble at shell-on prawns or a plate of toasted anchovy fingers or tuck into a generous charcoal-grilled steak; there's also excellent ham, tongue or beef to enjoy with salad or in a sandwich. Finish with prime Stilton or perhaps apple pie served with Devonshire clotted cream. No dogs. *Typical prices:* Dish of prawns £1·55 Charcoal-grilled rib of beef £5·20.☺ WC

East Grinstead — Gravetye Manor

81% £A

West Hoathly, West Sussex.
Sharpthorne (0342) 810567 ●
Map 7D8. Take M23 south to
junction 10. Then take A264
towards East Grinstead. Turn
off right onto B2028 to
Turner's Mill (Haywards

Heath). Follow signs for West Hoathly. Hotel is signposted ●
Bedrooms 14. En suite 14. With phone 14. With TV 14 ●
Confirm by arrangement

This creeper-clad Elizabethan manor house is a delightful hotel with a stunning setting, exemplary housekeeping and admirable staff. Owner Peter Herbert's attention to detail never wavers, even after 30 years. Public rooms abound in traditional country-house charm, with mellow oak panelling, superb mouldings, antiques and fine oils. Bedrooms are equally stylish and provide every conceivable comfort, from books and magazines to fresh flowers, mineral water and remote-control TVs (discreetly hidden behind tapestry screens). Attractively tiled bathrooms offer luxury toiletries and hairdryers. No children under seven. No dogs. *Amenities* garden, game fishing, croquet, laundry service.

East Grinstead	Gravetye Manor Restaurant

★★

West Hoathly, West Sussex. Sharpthorne
(0342) 810567 ● Map 7D8. See hotel entry
for directions ● Lunch 12.30–1.45. Dinner
7.30–9 ● Set L £15. About £70 for two

Truly memorable eating in a setting of dark-panelled elegance, with superb wines and skilled, unobtrusive service. Alan Garth's cooking is faultless in concept and preparation, his dishes a feast of fine flavours and fabulous sauces: fresh asparagus comes with its perfect accompaniment, a delicate sauce mousseline; terrine de foie gras de canard is served with a finely chopped Sauternes jelly; pan-fried Dover sole is matched magnificently with a timbale of crab and a light mustard sauce. *Specialities* smoked venison with red cabbage sauce, lamb served on aubergine with garlic sauce, carrot and hazelnut cake with apricot sauce. ☺.
⊏*OUTSTANDING* ♀ *WELL-CHOSEN* house wine.

Gatwick Airport	Gatwick Hilton International

£B 76%

West Sussex
Crawley (0293)
518080 ● Map
7B7. Follow
signs for the
airport. Hotel
is signposted
from there ● Bedrooms 333. En suite 333. With phone 333.
With TV 333. Confirm by 6 ● *Credit* Access, Amex, Diners,
Visa

Superb amenities for the traveller and businessman in this smooth-running modern hotel, which has a covered walkway to the main airport terminal and railway station. The large, plant-filled lobby contains a full-size replica of a Gypsy Moth biplane, and there are two bars. Bedrooms are fully sound-proofed and air-conditioned and have TVs that can call up flight information; bathrooms are unashamedly luxurious. *Amenities* sauna, indoor swimming pool, solarium, whirlpool bath, keep-fit equipment, dinner dance (fortnightly in winter), 24-hour lounge service, coffee shop (24 hours), valeting, laundry service, health & beauty clinic, kiosk.

Horley   Chequers Thistle Hotel

67%
£C

Brighton Road, Surrey. Crawley (0293)
786992 ● Map 7B7. Take M23 (Gatwick) to
junction 9. Follow signs for Reigate and
Horley onto Brighton Road (A23). Hotel is
on left ● Bedrooms 78. En suite 78. With
phone 78. With TV 78 ● Confirm by 6 ●
Credit Access, Amex, Diners, Visa

Situated just north of Gatwick airport, this is an old, half-
timbered coaching inn which extensions and improvements
have turned into a pleasantly comfortable hotel. There's a
stylishly furnished lounge-reception, where shelves of books
on either side of an open fireplace suggest a family library
rather than a hotel foyer. Ornaments and fresh flower
arrangements add to the homely atmosphere. The two bars
offer a choice of moods—one lively, the other more subdued.
Bedrooms, attractively refurbished with coordinating colour
schemes, are equipped with hairdryers, trouser presses and
tea-makers. *Amenities* garden, outdoor swimming pool, in-
house movies, transport for airport.

Horley   Gatwick Moat House

62%
£C

Longbridge Roundabout, Surrey. Horley
(0293) 785599 ● Map 7B7. Take M23
(Gatwick) to junction 9. Then take A23
towards Redhill. Hotel is just off the first
roundabout ● Bedrooms 120. En suite
120. With phone 120. With TV 120 ●
Confirm by 6 ● *Credit* Access, Amex,
Diners, Visa

Behind the functional facade the public rooms are attractive
and inviting at this modern three-storey hotel. Light woodwork
and green plants create a restful atmosphere in the foyer and
coffee shop area. Upstairs the smart lounge bar and
restaurant have stylish dark cane furnishings. Air-conditioned
bedrooms offer tea-makers, remote-control TVs and practical
bathrooms. Staff are cheerful and friendly, giving visitors the
kind of warm welcome not often found in airport hotels. There
is limited room service during the summer months, none at
all in winter. *Amenities* in-house movies, transport to airport,
coffee shop (2.30pm–11pm).

Horley   Gatwick Penta Hotel

£C 71%

Povey Cross Road, Surrey.
Crawley (0293) 785533 ●
Map 7B7. Take M23
(Gatwick) to junction 9. Then
take A23 towards Redhill.
Hotel is just off first
roundabout ● Bedrooms

260. En suite 260. With phone 260. With TV 260 ● Confirm by
6 ● *Credit* Access, Amex, Diners, Visa

A new leisure complex will suit travellers in need of brisk
revival at this streamlined modern hotel. If sleep is the priority,
the spacious bedrooms are soundproofed and air-conditioned. Bathrooms are spotlessly kept. Relaxing public areas
range from the leafy, leather-furnished foyer-lounge to the
smart coffee shop and plush Brighton Belle Bar decorated
with railway memorabilia. Self-contained and up-to-the minute
conference facilities available. *Amenities* garden, sauna,
indoor swimming pool, solarium, whirlpool bath, keep-fit
equipment, squash, discothèque (twice weekly), in-house
movies, kiosk, transport to airport, coffee shop (11am–6am),
laundry service.

Horley   Post House Hotel

62%
£C

Povey Cross Road, Horley, Surrey. Horley
(0293) 771621 ● Map 7B7. Take M23
(Gatwick) to junction 9. Then take A23
towards Redhill . Hotel is just off the first
roundabout ● Bedrooms 149. En suite
149. With phone 149. With TV 149 ●
Confirm by 6 ● *Credit* Access, Amex,
Diners, Visa

A five-storey purpose-built hotel providing pleasant, practical
accommodation. The building has recently been treated to
extensive refurbishment and a new block of 70 bedrooms is
under construction. Public rooms include a comfortable
sunken bar with baby grand piano. Decoration throughout is
smart if undistinguished. Standard bedrooms offer tea-
makers and mini-bars. Executive rooms run to further
gadgetry with hairdryers, trouser presses and remote-control
TVs—nice finishing touches are plants, chocolates and bath
toiletries. *Amenities* patio, outdoor swimming pool, transport
to airport, kiosk, coffee shop (10.30am–10.45pm), in-house
movies, laundry service.

Horley   Ye Olde Six Bells

(Food)

Church Road, Surrey. Horley (0293)
782209 ● Map 7B7. Take M23 (Gatwick) to
junction 9. Follow signs for Reigate (A23)
and then Horley. Turn first left off Horley
Road ● Last bar food 9.30pm ● *Credit*
Access, Amex, Diners, Visa ● *Brewery*
Vintage Inns. *Beers* Bass Bitter,
Charrington IPA; Worthington Bitter;
Guinness; Carling Black Label; Tennent's
Extra; cider

In summer you can sit outside on the lawn that runs down to the water's edge. Downstairs is a lovely unspoilt bar with low beamed ceiling and huge open fireplace. Upstairs in the Monk's Pantry, beneath splendid old roof timbers, you'll find excellent bar snacks—succulent cold meats, crisp salads and hot dishes like steak pie and veal korma. Sandwiches and puddings also available. Tables are candlelit in the evening, when there's a £2·50 minimum charge unless you eat in the bar downstairs. *Typical prices:* Pasta tricolor £2·40. Veal korma £4·50. ☕

Lowfield Heath   Gatwick Concorde Hotel

58%
£C

West Sussex. Crawley (0293) 33441 ●
Map 7B8. Take M23 (Gatwick) to junction
9. Then take A23, following signs for
Crawley, then Lowfield Heath and
Charlwood. Hotel is at next roundabout ●
Bedrooms 92. En suite 92. With phone 92.
With TV 92 ● Confirm by 6 ● *Credit*
Access, Amex, Diners, Visa ● Closed 24
December–2 January

Built in 1960, this hotel standing parallel to Gatwick's main runway is a useful stopover for travellers. Efficient sound-proofing and air conditioning keep things quiet and cool in the bedrooms, all of which have carpeted bathrooms, remote-control TVs and tea-makers. Top bedrooms on the runway side are more luxuriously furnished and enjoy good views of arrivals and departures. Decor throughout dates largely from the '60s and hardly seems modern now but there is a comfortable cocktail bar, a lively pub-style bar and a spacious, simply furnished foyer-lounge. *Amenities* garden, in-house movies, transport for airport.

Thornton Heath   Mamma Adele

23 Brigstock Road, Surrey. 01-683 2233 ●
Map 7C3. Take M23, then A23 towards
Croydon. Continue on A23 following signs
for Thornton Heath. Take A235 back
towards Croydon, then turn sharp left into
Brigstock Road ● Lunch 12–2.30. Dinner
7–11, Fri & Sat 7–11.30 ● About £30 for
two ● *Credit* Access, Amex, Diners, Visa ●
Closed L Mon & Sat, all Sun, Bank
Holidays, 4 weeks July/August & 1 week
Christmas

The enthusiastic Memons are a real asset at this attractive, unpretentious Italian restaurant. Kam Memon provides a warm welcome and looks after his customers attentively. His wife Adele does the cooking, emerging from her kitchen from time to time to deliver a hot dish. Her cooking is fairly simple and straightforward, though sound and reliable. A menu of mainly familiar favourites (spaghetti carbonara or alle vongole, tortellini alla panna, liver veneziana, veal escalope milanese, saltimbocca) is supplemented by specials like fresh asparagus, monkfish in garlic butter and duck breast with brandy sauce. Good vegetables and enjoyable sweets. ☺.

We do not necessarily recommend
the food at hotels listed in this guide.
If we recommend a hotel restaurant,
a separate entry is made.

JUNCTION
–8–

EXIT SIGNS

Travelling clockwise	A217	Sutton Reigate Kingston
Travelling anticlockwise	A217	Sutton Reigate Kingston

RESTAURANT

Cheam   Al San Vincenzo

52 Upper Mulgrave Road, Surrey. 01-661
9763 ● Map 7B4. Take A217 towards
Sutton. Follow signs for Cheam and the
railway station. Restaurant is on right ●
Lunch 12–2. Dinner 6.30–9.30 (Sat 6–10) ●
Set L & D £14.50. About £36 for two ●
Credit Access, Amex, Diners, Visa ●
Closed Sun (except Mothering Sun)

Vincenzo and Elaine Borgonzolo run this charming little
restaurant unaided and all dishes are cooked to order. Results
are certainly worth waiting for, with Vincenzo applying his
own very individual ideas to southern Italian traditions.
Describing his cooking as 'natural cuisine', he uses only the
very best raw materials (fresh, organically-grown vegetables
and hormone-free meat), ensuring by careful preparation that
natural flavours are fully retained. The delights are varied,
ranging from seafood casserole to quails with white grapes
and brandy sauce. Specials might include fresh tuna steak or
wild rabbit alla cacciatora. Delicious fresh fruit desserts.
Booking recommended. ✆.

Cheam   Superfish

64 The Broadway, Surrey. 01-643 6906 ●
Map 7B4. Take A217 towards Sutton. Turn
left after Cheam station into the High
Street. Turn second right for The
Broadway. Restaurant is on right ● Open
11.30–2 (Sat till 2.30) & 5.30–11 (Fri & Sat
5–11.30). Closed Sun & some Bank
Holidays

Aptly named, for the fish is indeed super at this bright,
cheerful restaurant in the centre of Cheam. Traditional
favourites cod, plaice and haddock are beautifully cooked
and served with smashing chips, good relishes and sauces
and a basket full of lovely hot French bread. Alternatives
include scampi, skate wings or halibut fillet, or 'Superbites'
—a mixture of haddock, cod and huss trimmings—all coated
in a light crisp batter. To round the meal off there are nice ice
creams served with French wafers. Friendly waiting staff.
Unlicensed. No dogs. *Typical prices:* Cod & chips £2·85
Scampi & chips £3·50.

Chipstead   Dene Farm

Outwood Lane, Surrey. Downland (073 75)
52661 ● Map 7B5. Take A217 towards
Sutton. Turn right onto B2032 towards
Coulsdon. Restaurant is on left ● Lunch
12–2. Dinner 7–10 ● Set L & D Tues–Fri
£13.50 About £46 for two ● *Credit* Access,
Amex, Diners, Visa ● Closed L Sat, D Sun,
all Mon, Bank Holidays except 25
December, 2 weeks August & 2 weeks
after Christmas

Despite its out-of-the-way location in a quiet, wooded valley
there's nothing unsophisticated about this delightful country
restaurant: only a few old beams strike a rustic note in the
otherwise elegant dining room. In these attractive surroundings chef Martin Radmall offers an imaginative selection of
expertly prepared dishes—orders are taken in the comfort of
the bar beforehand. Prime raw materials are behind such
inspired offerings as warm duck salad and chicory tartlets,
chicken breast stuffed with pistachio mousse and veal served
with noodles and a well-made tomato and basil sauce.
Delectable sweets and good wines. Impeccable service. ☺

Ewell   Superfish

9 Castle Parade, By-pass Road, Surrey.
01-393 3674 ● Map 7A4. Take A217
towards Sutton. Then take A240 and
follow signs for Ewell. Turn right onto
Ewell by-pass and then into the service
road (Castle Parade) ● Open 11.30–2 (Sat
till 2.30) & 5.30–11 (Fri & Sat 5–11.30).
Closed Sun & some Bank Holidays

Fresh from Billingsgate market, the fish served in this busy restaurant and takeaway is of outstanding quality—whether the generous portions of cod, plaice, skate, huss or halibut. Other attractions are the bright and cheerful decor and friendly, helpful staff. Expert cooking in pure beef dripping turns succulent steaks and fillets into mouth-watering meals. Accompaniments include crisp chips, assorted relishes and warm French bread. Excellent ice creams to follow. it's not surprising that this restaurant—one of a successful chain— has built up such a loyal following. No dogs. *Typical prices:* Cod & chips £2·85 Skate & chips £3·40. WC

Morden   Superfish

20 London Road, Surrey. 01-648 6908 ●
Map 7B3. Take A217 through Cheam
towards Sutton. Turn left at Rose Hill
roundabout, then first left again onto A24
at Morden roundabout. Restaurant is on
right ● Open 11.30–2 (Fri & Sat till 2.30) &
5.30–11 (Fri & Sat 5–11.30). Closed Sun &
Bank Holidays

An open-to-view frying area adds a lively note to this welcoming fish and chip shop-cum-restaurant, one of a popular chain. Ultra-fresh fish ranges from cod, haddock and plaice to skate, halibut and lemon sole. All frying is done in beef dripping, ensuring crisp, dry batter and excellent flavour. Good chips and scrumptious French bread. Red-checked tablecloths topped by white paper overlays provide a touch of class as do the quality ice creams with which you are invited to end your meal. No dogs. *Typical prices:* Cod & chips £2·85 Skate & chips £3·40. WC

Reigate   La Barbe

71 Bell Street, Surrey. Reigate (073 72)
41966 ● Map 7B6. Take A217 into Reigate.
Follow the one-way system (right into
Church Street, left into Bancroft Road and
left into Bell Street). Restaurant is 200
yards down on left ● Lunch 12–2. Dinner
7–10 ● Set L £11 Set D £17 incl. wine.
About £35 for two ● *Credit* Access, Amex,
Diners, Visa ● Closed L Sat & Mon, all Sun
& Bank Holidays

This cheerful little restaurant is just the place to recall the
flavours of a holiday in France. Bare brick walls, booth-style
seating and wicker lampshades set the tone of the bistro-
style interior. The cooking is confident with clear, fresh tastes
to the fore in dishes like pike mousse, chicken with tarragon
and porc à la normande. Old favourites such as frogs' legs
and snails are also available. The gratin dauphinois is good
and garlicky, and there's a nice choice of desserts including
crème de marrons and charlotte amandine. Note that evening
set menus include kir, wine, coffee and service. ☺

Reigate   Bridge House Hotel

57%
£D

Reigate Hill, Surrey. Reigate (073 72)
46801 ● Map 7B6. Take A217 towards
Reigate. Hotel is on right ● Bedrooms 30.
En suite 30. With phone 30. With TV 30 ●
Confirm by arrangement ● *Credit* Access,
Amex, Diners, Visa

High on Reigate Hill with extensive views over the town and
beyond, this is a modern hotel providing practical accommodation ideal for the business traveller or other short-stay
visitor. There is a comfortable bar and a large and busy
restaurant. The bedrooms have been recently refurbished
with bright matching curtains and wallpaper and smart
darkwood furniture; most have little balconies to take full
advantage of the views. En suite facilities are roomy and have
hairdryers and other bathtime accessories. Just one bedroom
(a small single) has a shower room. No dogs. *Amenities*
dancing (Tues–Sat), laundry service.

RESTAURANT

Sutton   Partners 23

23 Stonecot Hill, Surrey. 01-644 7743 ●
Map 7B4. Take A217 towards Sutton.
Take B279 off by-pass, then turn left into
Stonecot Hill. Restaurant is on left ● Lunch
12.30–2. Dinner 7.30–9.30 ● Set L £9.75
Set D £16.50 About £35 for two ● *Credit*
Access, Amex, Diners, Visa ● Closed L
Sat, all Sun & Mon, 2 weeks August & 25
December–early January

Amiable host Andrew Thomason and talented chef Tim McEntire make a winning team at this smart little restaurant in a shopping parade. Seasonally changing fixed-price menus are kept sensibly short with a choice of some five or six dishes per course. These are imaginative creations such as rillettes of game birds, medallion of monkfish with mussels and crab, and fillet of lamb with sweet peppers. Vegetables could sometimes do with a little less cooking. Desserts might include a beautifully light white chocolate mousse topped with dark chocolate sauce and chopped nuts. Excellent cheeseboard, with some unusual English varieties. ☺

RESTAURANT

Walton-on-the-Hill   Ebenezer Cottage

36 Walton Street, Surrey. Tadworth (073
781) 3166 ● Map 7A5. Take A217 towards
Sutton. Turn left onto B2220 to Walton-on-
the-Hill. Restaurant is in centre of the
village, behind a garage ● Lunch 12–1.45.
Dinner 7–9.30 ● Set L £10·50, Sun £11·25
Set D Tues–Thurs £14 About £50 for two ●
Credit Access, Amex, Diners, Visa ●
Closed D Sun, all Mon & 25 December–2
January

Menus at this charming restaurant in a 17th-century building offer a good selection of carefully prepared dishes. Prime raw materials are skilfully used in fairly safe and sober combinations—nothing too ambitious, yet at the same time there's a welcome absence of gimmickry and pretension. Typical items range from carrot and basil soup or chicken and leek soup to escalope of veal in a lime butter sauce, roast lamb in a pastry case. Dover sole in an orange and chervil sauce or goose breast with plums and brandy sauce. English farmhouse cheeses, well worth investigating. ☺. ♀ *WELL-CHOSEN* house wine.

JUNCTIONS
9–10

JUNCTION
–9–

EXIT SIGNS

Travelling clockwise	A3	London (SW) Kingston Guildford (Wisley RHS Gdns)
Travelling anticlockwise	A3	London (SW) Guildford

HOTEL

Dorking   Burford Bridge Hotel

£C70%

Box Hill,
Burford Bridge,
Surrey. Dorking
(0306) 884561
● Map 8D7.
Follow signs for
Dorking (A24)

for about 4 miles. Hotel is on left ● Bedrooms 52. En suite
52. With phone 52. With TV 52 ● Confirm by 6 ● *Credit*
Access, Amex, Diners, Visa

A distinctive long, low, white-painted building located at the
foot of Box Hill, this smartly decorated hotel dates back to
the 18th century. There's a traditional, comfortable air about
the day rooms, which feature one or two nice antiques. The
bar is pleasantly inviting, and there's a splendid function room
in an old tithe barn. Two of the bedrooms have four-posters
and military-style furniture; the rest sport modern units
incorporating mini-bars. Trouser presses and hairdryers are
standard, and bathrooms are good. The 20 rooms in the
garden suite are particularly well heated. *Amenities* garden,
outdoor swimming pool, laundry service.

78

Dorking Burford Bridge Hotel Lounge

Box Hill, Burford Bridge, Surrey. Dorking
(0306) 884561 ● Map 8D7. See hotel entry
for directions ● Open noon–10.30 ● *Credit*
Access, Amex, Diners, Visa

The lounge of this hotel is a comfortably elegant place. Delicious home-made cakes, scones and biscuits are available all day long and might include a creamy fresh plum cheesecake or a moist and crunchy walnut gâteau. Also on the menu are tasty savoury snacks like well-filled sandwiches (prawn, smoked salmon, roast beef, turkey) and a three-cheese platter with wholemeal bread, pickles, apple slices and salad. There's a particularly wide range of herbal teas, and set teas are served every afternoon. *Typical prices:* Set afternoon tea £6·25 Roast beef & horseradish sandwich £2. 🍵 ☙ WC

Dorking Punch Bowl Hotel

£D
54%

Reigate Road, Surrey. Dorking (0306)
889335 ● Map 8D7. Take A24 to Dorking
and follow signs for Horsham and Reigate
(do not turn off for town centre). Hotel is on
right ● Bedrooms 29. En suite 29. With
phone 29. With TV 29 ● Confirm by
arrangement ● *Credit* Access, Amex,
Diners, Visa

Enjoying fine views over Box Hill, this unpretentious hotel centres on an old, stone-built inn and has a cosy pub-style bar. A restaurant extension incorporates a cocktail bar/ lounge. Decor in these areas is a little tired but refurbishment is under way. Bedrooms, which are in a two-storey motel block across the car park, are pleasantly decorated with simple fitted furniture, remote-control TVs and quite roomy bathrooms. A bedroom extension is also envisaged. Modest comfort is the order of the day here, adequate for the needs of the overnight traveller. *Amenities* garden, laundry service.

HOTEL

Dorking White Horse Hotel

£D
58%

High Street, Surrey. Dorking (0306)
881138 ● Map 8D7. Take A24 into Dorking
town centre. Hotel is on right ● Bedrooms
68. En suite 68. With phone 68. With TV 68
● Confirm by 6 ● *Credit* Access, Amex,
Diners, Visa

An inn since 1750, the White Horse conceals abundant charm
and character behind its attractive coaching house frontage.
Oak timbers are a feature of the day rooms, which include
snug lounges and a cosy bar. An open fire burns in the main
lounge, creating an especially warm welcome in winter.
Bedrooms, almost half in a modern block overlooking the
pool, are of a fair size, and have tea-makers and remote-
control TVs with radio. Bathrooms are light and airy with
contemporary fittings; bath robes, foams and gels add a
touch of luxury. *Amenities* garden, outdoor swimming pool,
laundry service.

HOTEL

East Horsley Thatchers Hotel

£C/D
65%

Epsom Road, Surrey. East Horsley
(048 65) 4291 ● Map 8C6. Take A24
towards Dorking. Then take A246
signposted Guildford. Hotel is on right ●
Bedrooms 29. En suite 29. With phone 29.
With TV 29 ● Confirm by arrangement ●
Credit Access, Amex, Diners, Visa

This welcoming hotel, set in its own grounds, offers comfortable accommodation and youthful but friendly service.
Reception area and lounge are both well furnished and there
is a panelled bar in the corner of the lounge, where a pianist
plays in the evening. Bedrooms are prettily decorated with
light, airy colour schemes and coordinated fabrics, and have
fully tiled bathrooms. Most bedrooms are grouped around
the pool, away from the main building; five more luxurious
ones are in a charming old cottage. No dogs. *Amenities*
garden, outdoor swimming pool, laundry service.

East Horsley   Thatchers Hotel Restaurant

Epsom Road, Surrey. East Horsley
(048 65) 4291 ● Map 8C6. See hotel entry
for directions ● Lunch 12.30–2.30, Sun
12.30–2. Dinner 7.30–9.30, Sun 7.30–9 ●
Set L £9·50. Set D £10·50. About £40 for
two ● *Credit* Access, Amex, Diners, Visa

A light, pretty and relaxing setting for enjoying capable, often imaginative cooking. Textures and flavours are carefully contrasted and balanced in a starter like steamed scallops in puff pastry with a Pernod and dill sauce. Breast of duck with glazed apples and a green peppercorn sauce is a typical main dish, the duck pink and tender, the sauce nicely seasoned and textured. Unfortunately vegetables are not quite so good. Tempting desserts, though, which include a light and airy banana mousse with mango syrup and tropical fruits. Very good cellar, with notable burgundies and Alsace wines. ☕. ♀ *WELL-CHOSEN* house wine.

Gomshall   Black Horse

(B&B)
£F

Station Road, Surrey. Shere (048 641)
2242 ● Map 8C7. Take A24 to Dorking.
Turn right onto A25 for Guildford. Follow
road for 5 miles into Gomshall ●
Bedrooms 6 ● Check-in all day ● *Credit*
Diners, Visa ● *Brewery* Young. *Beers*
Young's Best Bitter, Special Bitter;
Beamish; Young's Premium Lager; John
Young's London Lager; cider

There's a solid, dependable air about this late 17th-century roadside inn, which stands in an area of great natural beauty. Heavy carved antique chairs, sturdy tables and a coal fire give character and warmth to the bar. Bedrooms are attractively furnished with matching (or toning) duvet covers, curtains and lampshades. All have washbasins, electric blankets and plug-in heaters and tea-makers. The residents' lounge is light, spacious and comfortable and boasts a large colour TV. Children are very welcome in the pub at lunchtime, but no under-12s overnight. Patio and garden.

RESTAURANT

Surbiton   Chez Max

85 Maple Road, Surrey. 01-399 2365 ●
Map 8D4. Take A243 towards London.
Follow signs for Surbiton railway station.
Turn left at station and then first right ●
Lunch 12.30–2. Dinner 7.30–10.30 ● Set L
£15. About £52 for two ● *Credit* Access,
Amex, Diners, Visa ● Closed L Sat, all Sun
& Mon, Good Friday, 2 weeks August & 24
December–7 January

Max Markarian, a former protégé of Prue Leith, set up his own restaurant in this quiet tree-lined street some three years ago and has never looked back. Decorated in smart pastel shades and stylishly furnished, the interior creates a relaxing atmosphere in which to enjoy Max's imaginative and occasionally brilliant cooking. The ambitious French menu, which changes regularly, includes dishes such as delicate salmon quenelles with scallops and a julienne of vegetables, fillet steak with truffles and a Madeira sauce, and lamb noisettes accompanied by a courgette mousse. Desserts can be rather less exciting. Service is welcoming and pleasant. ☺

JUST A BITE

Surbiton   Fortunes

4 Victoria Road, Surrey. 01-399 6909 ●
Map 8D4. Take A243 towards London.
Follow signs for Surbiton railway station.
Restaurant is opposite station ● Open
11am–11pm. Closed 25 & 26 December

Service is friendly and the atmosphere relaxed at this classic hamburger restaurant with bare brick walls and bentwood chairs. Chargrilled burgers, quarter- or half-pounders, come plain and simple or with tasty toppings like chilli and red beans or garlic and parsley butter. There's even a special burger for vegetarians. Steaks include the T-bone special weighing in at a pound, and there are other popular favourites such as spaghetti, scampi, quiche and chicken Kiev. Sunday roast lunch. Nice garlic bread and salads. No dogs. *Typical prices:* Chilliburger £3 Garlic mushrooms £1·45. WC

Surbiton   Liberty Bell

158 Ewell Road, Surrey. 01-390 7564 ●
Map 8D4. Take A243 towards London.
Turn right onto A3 (Kingston by-pass) and
follow signs for Tolworth and Surbiton
(A240). Bear right at fork. Restaurant is on
left ● Open noon–2.30 & 6–11. Closed Sun
& 1 week Christmas ● *Credit* Access, Visa

A busy, informal and instantly likable restaurant with a strong
Edwardian feel to the decor. Original stained-glass panels
and cast-iron pillars date from the time when this was a music
shop called Bells. The menu combines a mid-Atlantic selection
– guacamole, chilli con carne, burgers and steaks – with
interesting daily specials such as beef and vegetable soup,
lamb cutlets hollandaise and breast of chicken with a good
Dijon mustard sauce. The usual range of puds like cheesecake
and ice cream sundaes. Friendly, speedy service. *Typical
prices:* Pork chops in red wine & coriander £5·25 Vegetarian
rösti 80p. WC

Surbiton   Oak

(Food)

Maple Road, Surrey. 01-399 1662 ● Map
8D4. Take A243 towards London. Follow
signs for Surbiton railway station. Turn left
at station and then first right ● *Brewery*
Charrington. *Beers* Bass Bitter,
Charrington IPA; Guinness; Carling Black
Label; Tennent's Extra; cider

On a corner site in a tree-lined road, this is a pleasant, roomy
place for enjoying a tasty lunchtime snack. Rag-painted dado
panelling and wooden Venetian blinds create a stylish interior
and there's an appetising display of cold foods – ham, beef,
pâté, Coronation turkey and egg mayonnaise. The choice of
hot dishes might range from freshly-baked quiche to stuffed
peppers and Lancashire lamb pie. To round things off, there's
a daily pud such as apple and orange flan. Cheerful friendly
service. Garden. *Typical prices:* Lancashire lamb pie £2·20
Egg mayonnaise £1·50. No bar food eves or Sun. ✑

JUNCTION –10–

EXIT SIGNS

Travelling clockwise	A3	London (SW) Guildford
Travelling anticlockwise	A3	London (SW) Kingston Guildford

HOTEL

Bramley	Bramley Grange Hotel

£C/D
64%

Horsham Road, Near Guildford, Surrey.
Guildford (0483) 893434 ● Map 8A8. Take
A3 to Guildford. Follow signs for 'other
routes' (not town centre). Then take A281
towards Horsham. Hotel is on right ●
Bedrooms 21. En suite 19. With phone 21.
With TV 21 ● Confirm by 6 ● *Credit*
Access, Amex, Diners, Visa

Housekeeping is a particularly strong point at this appealing hotel, smartly modern behind a long mock-Tudor façade. A copper-hooded gas log fire warms the reception/lounge area, and an eye-catching gilt chandelier sets the tone of the bar, which overlooks the large, well-kept garden and the wooded hillside beyond. Spacious bedrooms, all simply furnished with white laminated units, are kept spotlessly clean; lots of little extras are thoughtfully provided, ranging from sewing kits to plasters. Sparkling modern bathrooms are also well stocked – offering shampoos, shower caps, even soap flakes. No dogs. *Amenities* garden, croquet, putting, tennis.

Cobham   Ladbroke Seven Hills Hotel

£B/C
60%

Seven Hills Road South, Surrey. Cobham
(093 26) 4471 ● Map 8C5. Take A3
towards London and then A245 towards
Cobham. Hotel is signposted ● Bedrooms
114. En suite 114. With phone 114. With TV
114 ● Confirm by 6 ● *Credit* Access,
Amex, Diners, Visa

This comfortable modern hotel, set in extensive wooded grounds, is a favourite conference venue, especially popular for its leisure facilities. Public areas include two jolly bars, one overlooking the garden. Practically furnished bedrooms decorated in pleasant pastel shades have tea-makers and direct-dial phones; superior, executive-style rooms in the newly-completed garden wing offer extra accessories – trouser presses, hairdryers and good writing surfaces. Bathrooms in the old house are fairly basic, those in the new wing more luxurious and better equipped – some even with whirlpool baths. *Amenities* garden, sauna, tennis, squash, dancing (Fri, Sat), 24-hour lounge service, helipad.

Cobham   Plough

(Food)

Plough Lane, Surrey. Cobham (0932)
62514. ● Map 8C5. Take A3 towards
London and follow signs for Cobham town
centre (A245). Turn right into Downside
Bridge Road, then first right again after the
bridge ● Last bar food 9pm ● *Credit*
Access, Visa ● *Brewery* Courage. *Beers*
Courage Best Bitter, Directors Bitter; John
Smith's Bitter; Guinness; Hofmeister;
Kronenbourg; cider

Whether you eat out in the garden or in the beamed lounge of this charming 500-year-old pub near Downside Bridge, you soon realise that food is important here, especially at lunch-time. The choice ranges from a woodman's lunch (with succulent home-cooked gammon) through sandwiches and salads to grills and basket meals. Lunchtime extras include jacket potatoes and hot specials like meat pies and lasagne. Children are very welcome and will be amused by the goat and rabbits kept in the garden. In summer there's a barbecue. *Typical prices:* Liver & bacon casserole £2·10 Steak pie £1·95. ☻

HOTEL

Cobham — Woodlands Park Hotel

£C
64%

Woodlands Lane, Stoke D'Abernon,
Surrey. Oxshott (037 284) 3933 ● Map
8C5. Take A3 towards London and then
A245 through Cobham towards
Leatherhead. Hotel is on right ● Bedrooms
32. En suite 32. With phone 32. With TV 32
● Confirm by 6 ● *Credit* Access, Amex,
Diners, Visa ● Closed 10 days after
Christmas

This grand late Victorian mansion was once the home of F. C. Bryant, whose father regularly entertained Edward VII, then Prince of Wales. Much of the original character of the house has been retained. The Grand Hall with its vaulted stained-glass ceiling and galley doubles as a comfortable lounge and bar. Most splendid among the function rooms is an ornate Louis XV style salon. Attractive bedrooms vary in size and shape and range from elegantly traditional to smartly modern, all with good bath or shower rooms. There are also two magnificent suites, the first equipped with a jacuzzi. *Amenities* garden, tennis, clay-pigeon shooting.

JUST A BITE

Compton — Old Congregational Tea Shop

Near Guildford, Surrey. Guildford (0483)
810682 ● Map 8A7. Take A3 to Guildford.
On leaving Guildford, follow signs for
Compton. Teashop is on left ● Open
10.30–5.30. Closed Mon (except Bank
Holidays), Tues & 1 week Christmas

Sally Porter's home and tea shop was once a Congregational church but now provides welcome refreshment for travellers, especially on summer weekends and bank holidays. At times like this, full use is made of the garden, with its cheerful profusion of flowers and shrubs. The menu could hardly be simpler: tea, coffee and soft drinks to accompany gorgeous scones served with thick cream – gallons of it brought over from nearby Loseley Farm – and lovely home-made jam; delicious home-baked cakes and cheesecake; soup; Welsh rarebit; toasted sandwiches. Unlicensed. *Typical prices:* Welsh rarebit 85p Coffee & walnut cake 55p. ● WC

East Molesey · Le Chien Qui Fume

107 Walton Road, Surrey. 01-979 7150 ●
Map 8D4. Take A3 towards London, then
follow signs for Esher (A307) and Hampton
Court (A309). Turn left at Hampton Court
railway station onto A3050 for East
Molesey. Restaurant is close to Molesey
police station ● Lunch 12–2. Dinner 7–11 ●
Set L £6·50. About £42 for two ● *Credit*
Access, Amex, Diners, Visa ● Closed Sun,
Bank Holidays & 3 weeks August

Outrageous cartoons of the eponymous dog line the walls of this long-established restaurant in the Surrey/London suburbs. It's run by the Dioli brothers who, despite their Italian roots, prefer to offer a good choice of capably prepared French dishes. Giancarlo, the elder brother, cooks – you can see him at work in the open-plan kitchen moulded out of the centre of the restaurant. The standard choice of popular items like sole bonne femme, chicken Kiev or ballotine de canard is supplemented by daily specials. Vegetables are carefully cooked, and well-kept cheeses make a good finish. Desserts may be less reliable. ☺

East Molesey · Langan's Bar & Grill

3 Palace Gate Parade, Hampton Court,
Surrey. 01-979 7891 ● Map 8D4. Take A3
towards London then follow signs for
Esher (A307) and Hampton Court (A309).
The parade is on left 50 yds from Hampton
Court Bridge ● Open noon–2.30 & 7–11
(Fri & Sat till 11.30, Sun till 10.30). Closed
25 & 26 December ● *Credit* Access, Amex,
Diners, Visa

A smart new brasserie where you can order anything from a single course to a full meal. The menu is interesting and varied, reflecting some of the imaginative style of Peter Langan's other restaurants. Starters might include deep-fried Brie with cranberry mousse or baked eggs topped by sherried chicken livers, while main courses could range from Cumberland sausages with onion sauce and mashed potatoes to poached salmon with a lovely sauce of morels. Super fresh vegetables, delicious sweets; cheeseboard. No dogs. *Typical prices:* Scallops wrapped in bacon with béarnaise sauce £3·20 Rosettes of pork with apple & Calvados £5·75. ☺ WC

East Molesey — Lantern

20 Bridge Road, Surrey. 01-979 1531 ●
Map 8D4. Take A3 towards London and
then A307 through Esher. Turn left for
Esher railway station and follow road into
Molesey. Turn right into Bridge Road ●
Lunch 12.30–2.15. Dinner 7–11 ● Set L
£7·50 & £11·95. Set D £12·75 & £15·95.
About £42 for two ● *Credit* Access, Amex,
Diners, Visa ● Closed L Mon & Sat, all Sun,
Bank Holidays & August

Peter Morphew can be relied upon to produce mouth-watering meals at this attractive little French restaurant. A shelf of fine culinary books within reach of one table gives patrons a hint of delights to come. The menu itself is no less interesting, ranging from garlic snails, crab mousse with melon and grapefruit and preserved duck with celery purée to veal with pink peppercorns in a cream and brandy sauce, grilled Dover sole and steak with three flavoured butters. Obvious care is taken with both preparation and presentation. Delicious sweets from a well-laden trolley. Simpler lunchtime carte.

East Molesey — Superfish

90 Walton Road, Surrey. 01-979 2432 ●
Map 8D4. Take A3 towards London, then
follow signs for Esher (A307) and Hampton
Court (A309). Turn left at Hampton Court
railway station, then right at the end into
Walton Road. Restaurant is beyond police
station on left ● Open 11.30–2 (Sat till 2.30)
& 5.30–11 (Fri & Sat 5–11.30). Closed Sun
& some Bank Holidays

Located in a busy parade of shops and with a popular takeaway counter as well, this is one of a chain of restaurants noted for the super-freshness of their fish. Sparkling fresh decor, white paper table covers and cut flowers reinforce the bright and breezy image. Succulent cod in batter comes with crisp chunky chips, French bread, relish tray and sauces. Haddock and plaice are equally good, and the choice may also include scampi, halibut and lemon sole. To finish, there's a selection of ice creams. Friendly service. No dogs. *Typical prices:* Cod & chips £2·85 Scampi & chips £3·50. WC

East Molesey   Vecchia Roma

57 Bridge Road, Surrey. 01-979 5490 ●
Map 8D4. Take A3 towards London and
then A307 through Esher. Turn left for
Esher railway station and follow road into
Molesey. Turn right into Bridge Road ●
Lunch 12–2.15. Dinner 7–11.15 ● Set L
£7·25. Sun £8·25. Set D £11·50. About £38
for two ● *Credit* Access, Diners, Visa ●
Closed L Sat & 26 December

A colourful Italian restaurant offering a large variety of dishes, both familiar – lasagne, veal escalope milanese, calf's liver with sage – and less usual, such as sole stuffed with scampi and prawns or lamb with black cherries. You are unlikely to go wrong if you try the daily specials: crespolini al forno – light pancakes encasing creamed spinach – might be followed by cuscinetto ben dormire – rolled veal escalope with a tasty filling of mozzarella and chopped onion. Adolfo Fiore's cooking is consistently capable and he passes the vegetable test with flying colours. Service is both friendly and skilful. ⊜
⟁ *WELL-CHOSEN* house wine.

Effingham   Plough

(Food)

Orestan Lane, Surrey. Bookham (0372)
58121 ● Map 8C6. Follow signs for
Guildford (A3), then for Effingham. Orestan
Lane is on right 1½ miles beyond Effingham
railway station ● Last bar food 8.30pm ●
Brewery Courage. *Beers* Courage Best
Bitter, Directors Bitter; Guinness;
Hofmeister; cider

Imaginative bar snacks are carefully prepared and full of flavour at this smartly white-painted pub with a pretty little garden at the back. Regular favourites like pâté, smoked mackerel, sandwiches and savoury pies are supplemented by a blackboard menu. This offers interesting daily specials such as cream of lettuce soup, crab and asparagus vol-au-vent, stuffed courgettes with cheese sauce, liver with sage and onion topping, mushroom and prawn gratin and haddock pasta. Nice sweets include trifle and treacle tart. *Typical prices:* Stuffed courgettes with cheese sauce £1·95 Prawn & asparagus pancake with salad £2. No bar food Sun. ⊜

RESTAURANT

Esher	Good Earth

14 High Street, Surrey. Esher (0372) 62489
● Map 8D5. Take A3 towards London,
then A307 into Esher. Restaurant is on
right ● Lunch 12–2.30, Sun 12.30–3.
Dinner 6–11.30, Sun 6–11 ● Set L £12. Set
D £14. About £36 for two ● *Credit* Access,
Amex, Diners, Visa ● Closed 24–27
December

A stylish, well-run restaurant, sibling of the three London Good Earths and sharing their multi-regional Chinese menu. There's a splendid choice of well-prepared dishes, from satay and sesame prawns to Cantonese-style steamed fish and beef in oyster sauce. One might start with steamed dumplings of pork, prawns and water chestnuts or with baked crab with ginger and spring onions. To follow it could be the excellent crispy duck or a delicate dish of chicken poached in its own stock. Spicy Szechuan aubergines are one of many vegetables dishes, and there are interesting set menus for two or more.

RESTAURANT

Esher	Le Pierrot

63 High Street, Surrey. Esher (0372) 63191
● Map 8D5. Take A3 towards London,
then A307 into Esher. Restaurant is on left
opposite the post office ● Lunch 12.15–
2.30. Dinner 7.15–10.30 ● Set L £6·50. Set
D £9·45. About £38 for two ● *Credit*
Access, Amex, Diners, Visa ● Closed L
Sat, all Sun, Bank Holidays & 1 week
January

Chef-patron Jean-Pierre Brichot labours behind the scenes in this attractive little restaurant, creating an interesting variety of French dishes, Mme Brichot, assisted by her team of French waiters, manages the front of the house with great charm and efficiency. The twice-weekly accordion player, despite his authentic French beret, is in fact English. Croustade of quail's eggs or crab mousse with cucumbers could start your meal, followed perhaps by fillet steak vigneronne or sliced breast of duckling with a blackcurrant and cassis sauce. Nice crisp vegetables. Desserts include honey and lemon pancakes, and there's a good choice of French cheeses. ☺

Guildford	Angel Hotel

£C/D
61%

High Street, Surrey. Guildford (0483)
64555 ● Map 8A7. Take A3 to Guildford.
Follow signs for Guildford town centre.
Turn left at bottom of Woodbridge Road,
then second left off roundabout ●
Bedrooms 27. En suite 27. With phone 27.
With TV 27 ● Confirm by 6 ● *Credit*
Access, Amex, Diners, Visa

Staff are friendly and welcoming at this well-maintained half-timbered inn. The oldest part is the 13th-century stone-vaulted restaurant but the lounge with its fine old oak galleries and Jacobean fireplace is perhaps even more impressive. Breakfast is served in the bright and cheerful coffee shop. A maze of corridors leads to the thoughtfully appointed bedrooms, which vary greatly in size. Some are furnished with antiques (including a four-poster) but most have standard fitted units. All offer remote-control TV and tea-makers. Good private bathrooms throughout, well supplied with toiletries. *Amenities* coffee shop (7.30am–10pm), laundry service.

Guildford	Richoux

17 The Friary, Surrey. Guildford (0483)
502998 ● Map 8A7. Take A3 to Guildford.
Follow signs for Guildford town centre,
then for Horsham (via Woodbridge Road).
Bear right at the fork. Friary centre is on
left just before bus station ● Open 9–6.
Closed Sun & Bank Holidays (except 1
January & Good Fri) ● *Credit* Access,
Amex, Diners, Visa

Brass chandeliers, mirrors and plants provide a smart setting for light refreshments at this Richoux establishment on the top floor of the Friary shopping centre. A few of the marble-effect-tables are set on the concourse outside. Waitresses in long aprons and frilly caps will serve you everything from breakfasts, club sandwiches, burgers, steak and kidney pie or salads to cream cakes, pastries and gâteaux from the trolley. Children's menu features fish fingers, spaghetti and sausages, beans and chips and there's a choice of ice creams. No dogs. *Typical prices:* Chicken & ham pie £3·25 Afternoon tea £1·95. WC

RESTAURANT

Guildford   Rumwong

16 London Road, Surrey. Guildford (0483)
36092 ● Map 8A7. Take A3 to Guildford
and follow signs for the town centre.
Restaurant is opposite Civic Hall ● Lunch
12–2.45. Dinner 6–10.45 ● About £30 for
two ● *Credit* Access, Visa ● Closed Mon, 2
days New Year, 1st 2 weeks August & 3
days Christmas

Colourful parasols hanging overhead and lampshades styled
like coolie hats give an Oriental feel to this Thai restaurant,
which stands in a parade of shops opposite the Civic Hall.
The menu lists a wide range of excellent dishes and offers
helpful guidance on how to construct a traditional Thai meal,
even giving suggestions for accompanying drinks. The hot
and sour soups and spicy salads are specialities. More
elaborate dishes include barbecued beef quenelles marinated
in chilli sauce and roast duck with pickled ginger and
cucumber. There are also one-plate rice and noodle dishes,
ideal for quick lunches and suppers.

PUB

Ripley   Anchor

(Food)

High Street, Surrey. Guildford (0483)
224120 ● Map 8B6. Take A3 towards
Guildford. Leave at first slip road and
follow signs for Ripley ● *Brewery* Friary
Meux. *Beers* Friary Meux Traditional
Bitter; Ind Coope Burton Ale; Guinness;
Löwenbräu; Skol; cider

With the opening of the A3 Guildford by-pass some years ago
Ripley once more became a peaceful Surrey village. At its
centre stands this 700-year-old half-timbered pub with cosy
low-beamed bars. Landlady Christine Beale does all the
cooking herself, producing plain wholesome lunchtime fare.
Her hearty soups and tasty savoury pies are especially
popular, but simple snacks like sandwiches, ploughman's,
pâté and salads are also available. Beef curry is a typical daily
special and there's a traditional roast on Sunday. Patio.
Typical prices: Steak pie with vegetables £2·25 Ham salad
£2·50 (No bar food eves). ◔

Ripley   Clock House

Portsmouth Road, Surrey. Guildford (0483)
224777 ● Map 8B6. Take A3 towards
Guildford. Leave at first slip road and
follow signs for Ripley. Restaurant is on
right in centre of village ● Lunch 12.30–2.
Dinner 7–9.30 ● Set L & D from £12, Sat
£28. About £48 for two ● *Credit* Access,
Amex, Diners, Visa ● Closed L Sat, D Sun,
all Mon & 25 December

Erik Michel turned to cooking after training as an artist, and presentation is an important element in his fine French cooking. Strong, forthright flavours highlight dishes like quenelles de brochet with lobster sauce and saddle of lamb with a mint sabayon. Corn-fed chicken is particularly tender and succulent, served, like other main courses, with crisp young vegetables. Sweets range from simple sorbets to caramelised strawberries with a fluffy eau de vie de framboise sauce and spun sugar. The beamed restaurant is roomy and comfortable, with nice pictures about the walls. Concise list of good wines, best in burgundy. ℮

Ripley   Seven Stars

(Food)

Newark Lane, Surrey. Guildford (0483)
225128 ● Map 8B6. Take A3 towards
Guildford. Leave at first slip road and
follow signs for Ripley. Turn right at
crossroads in centre of village ● Last bar
food 9pm ● *Brewery* Friary Meux. *Beers*
Friary Meux Best Bitter, Mild; Benskins;
Ind Coope Bitter; Guinness; Löwenbräu;
cider

Prize-winning pizzas are among the tasty home-prepared snacks served in this cheerful roadside pub. Landlord Rodney Dean sets high standards in the kitchen and stays closely involved on the food front. Daily specials marked up on the blackboard could include lasagne (made with a good meaty sauce and served with a crisp green salad), jumbo sausage, cauliflower cheese, seafood platter and chilli. To finish, there might be apricot crumble or a splendid chocolate rum trifle. Also freshly-made roast-beef sandwiches, soup in winter and a lunchtime cold buffet. Garden. *Typical prices:* Goulash with salad £1·30 Special pizza £2·10. ℮

PUB

Thames Ditton   Albany

(Food)

Queens Road, Surrey. 01-398 7031 ● Map
8C4. Take A3 towards London, then A307
through Esher onto Hampton Court Way
(A309). Follow signs for Thames Ditton.
Turn left by railway station, right at
crossroads and first left again ● *Brewery*
Charrington. *Beers* Bass Bitter,
Charrington IPA; Fuller's ESB; Guinness;
Grolsch; Tennent's Extra; cider

A large late Victorian pub in a marvellous location by the river.
From the terrace you can look across to the opposite bank
and glimpse Hampton Court Palace through the trees. Inside
there's a welcoming atmosphere with bowls of fresh flowers,
open fires and a magnificent spread of food. Platters of rare
roast beef, ham and turkey jostle for space on the cold table
alongside raised pies, salmon mousse, pâtés and salads. A
small selection of hot dishes might include moussaka and a
pie. No puds. *Typical prices:* Coronation turkey salad £2·95
Cassoulet £2·20 (No bar food eves or Sun). ☺

JUST A BITE

Thames Ditton   Skiffers

High Street, Surrey. 01-398 5540 ● Map
8C4. Take A3 towards London, then A307
through Esher onto Hampton Court Way
(A309). Follow signs for Thames Ditton ●
Open noon–2. Closed Sun, Mon, 26
December & 1st week January ● *Credit*
Access, Amex, Diners, Visa

Getting top-quality meat for their attractive, bistro-style
restaurant is no problem for Keith and Liz Harding, for they
also own the butcher's shop next door. Liz's consistently
enjoyable cooking spans a good range, from French onion
soup and coarse country pâté to seafood gratin, succulent
rack of lamb and tender medallions of pork with a well-
flavoured mustard sauce. Vegetables are made a lot more
interesting than usual (honey-roast parsnips, courgettes with
bacon, carrots with raisins, ratatouille, cauliflower cheese),
and nice sweets include a spicy Dutch apple pie. *Typical
prices:* Curried beef £2·85 French onion soup £1·20. ☺ 🍴
WC

Tolworth   Superfish

59 The Broadway, Surrey. 01-390 2868 ●
Map 8D4. Take A3 towards London. Turn
left into the Broadway (signposted
Kingston and Tolworth). Restaurant is on
right ● Open 11.30–2.30 (Sat till 3) & 5.30–
11.30 (Fri & Sat 5–11.30). Closed Sun, Mon
& Bank Holidays (except Good Friday)

In a parade of shops almost below Tolworth Tower, this
pleasantly informal fish and chip restaurant is one of a highly
successful chain, all noted for the excellence of their fish.
Choose from cod, plaice or haddock, or perhaps scampi,
huss or halibut. Company policy is to fry in best-quality beef
dripping, producing wonderful crisp and tasty batter and
chips. Friendly, helpful staff are a major asset here, and nice
touches include a generous-sized bread basket full of hot
french sticks. Ice creams range from vanilla to coconut. No
dogs. *Typical prices:* Cod & chips £2·85 Scampi & chips
£3·50. WC

West Byfleet   Superfish

51 Old Woking Road, Surrey. Byfleet
(093 23) 40366 ● Map 8B5. Take A3
towards London. Take A245 through
Byfleet and beyond the flyover. Parvis
Road leads into Old Woking Road.
Restaurant is just beyond on left ● Open
11.30–2 (Sat till 2.30) & 5.30–10.30 (Fri &
Sat 5.30–11). Closed Sun & some Bank
Holidays

The latest in a small chain of restaurants offering, as the
souvenir menu has it, 'delectable fish and chips fried in the
Yorkshire way'. Beef dripping is the medium for frying, and
the fish includes cod, haddock, rockfish and scampi, joined
by skate, halibut, whole plaice and whole sole on the bone
when available. Cod portions are offered in three sizes. The
French bread is good and crusty, and sauces and pickles are
available from the trolley. Sweets comprise a selection of ice
creams. No dogs. *Typical prices:* Cod & chips £2·30 Halibut
& chips £3·95. WC

West Clandon · Onslow Arms

Near Guildford, Surrey. Guildford (0483)
222447 ● Map 8B7. Take A3 towards
Guildford and then follow signs for Wisley
Garden Centre. Turn onto A247 for West
Clandon. Pub is on left just beyond railway
station ● Lunch 12.30–2. Dinner 7.30–10 ●
Set L £8·95, Sun £9·95. About £50 for two
● *Credit* Access, Amex, Diners, Visa ●
Closed L some Sats, D Sun, all Mon & 1
week Christmas

A busy pub restaurant with plenty of dark wooden beams, gilt-framed paintings and old-world charm. A real fire burns in the adjoining cocktail bar and is even used to spit-roast the occasional duck! There's an interesting and fairly ambitious French menu, ranging from quail's egg croustade to monkfish with chive sauce, châteaubriand béarnaise and partridge with mangoes. Cooking is reliably good, with careful selection of raw materials and nice attention to detail. This is a popular place for wedding receptions, which explains why the restaurant is often closed at lunchtime on Saturdays. ⊖ ♀ *WELL-CHOSEN* house wine.

Our inspectors never book
in the name of Egon Ronay's Guides;
they disclose their identity only
after paying their bills.

JUNCTIONS 11–13

JUNCTION –11–

EXIT SIGNS

Travelling clockwise	A320	Woking
	A317	Chertsey
Travelling anticlockwise	A320	Chertsey
		Woking

Shepperton   Anchor Hotel

(B&B)
£E

Church Square, Middlesex. Walton-on-Thames (0932) 221618 ● Map 10D3. Follow signs for Chertsey (A317). Continue straight on after roundabout and turn right at T-junction onto B375. Church Square is on right, $1\frac{1}{2}$ miles after Chertsey Bridge ● Bedrooms 24. With bath/shower 24. With TV 24. Check-in all day ● *Credit* Access, Amex, Diners, Visa ● Free House. *Beers* Eldridge Pope Dorset IPA, Royal Oak; Flowers Original Bitter; Faust Export, Lager, Heineken; cider

This 400-year old inn stands just a few yards from the Thames in a little square that was once notorious for its bare-fisted prize fights. The inn itself is a friendly, well-run place, and the bar, with its original beams, lovely carved oak panelling and subtle lighting, is a very pleasant spot for a drink. Traffic outside is busy at times and all bedrooms are double-glazed. Sizes vary enormously but colour schemes are simple and furnishings mainly modern. All rooms offer direct-dial phones, tea-makers (with radios) and neatly fitted shower rooms. Patio. Children welcome.

Shepperton — Thames Court

(Food)

Towpath, Middlesex. Walton-on-Thames
(0932) 221957 ● Map 10D3. Follow signs
for Chertsey (A317). Continue straight on
after roundabout, and turn right at T-
junction onto B375. Turn right after
Chertsey Bridge into Dockett Eddy Lane.
This leads to the Towpath ● Last bar food
9.30pm ● Free House. *Beers* Bass Bitter,
Charrington IPA; Stones Bitter; Guinness;
Carling Black Label; Tennent's Extra; cider

This handsome brick-built pub enjoys a delightful garden setting by the Thames at Shepperton weir. The spacious panelled bar is designed on two levels, linked by a spiral staircase. Different areas are designated for food and drink, with a tempting cold buffet laid out in the food section at lunchtime (also on summer evenings). Two or three hot dishes are always available too – perhaps beef curry and roast pork – as well as soups, jacket potatoes, sandwiches and sweets like pear flan and Pavlova. Children welcome. *Typical prices:* Wholemeal courgette & prawn quiche £1·10 Roast beef & Yorkshire pudding £3. 🍽

Shepperton — Warren Lodge Hotel

£E

Church Square, Walton-on-Thames,
Middlesex. (0932) 242972 ● Map 10D3.
Follow signs for Chertsey (A317). Continue
straight on after roundabout and turn right
at T-junction onto B375 towards
Shepperton. Hotel is on right ● Bedrooms
46. En suite 41. With phone 46. With TV 46
● Confirm by arrangement ● *Credit*
Access, Amex, Diners, Visa

Walnut and mulberry trees flourish in the garden of this attractive 18th-century hotel, owned and run by Douglas Gordon for the past 20 years. On one side is the old Church Square, on the other the garden and terrace overlooking the Thames. There is an inviting reception area with chairs grouped around a gas-fired 'open log' fire. The cosy bar doubles as a lounge outside licensing hours. Simple white bedrooms (housed in two modern extensions) have practical units, direct-dial phones and radio-alarms. Most have private shower rooms attached, though 14 have bathrooms. No dogs. *Amenities* garden.

HOTEL

Weybridge   Oatlands Park Hotel

£D
57%

146 Oatlands Drive, Surrey. Weybridge
(0932) 47242 ● Map 10D3. Follow signs for
Chertsey and then Weybridge (A317). Take
A3050 towards Walton-on-Thames. Hotel
is on left ● Bedrooms 130. En suite 98.
With phone 130. With TV 130 ● Confirm by
6 ● *Credit* Access, Amex, Diners, Visa

This large, rambling hotel, part period, part modern, stands
in its own grounds with an imposing portico at the front and
an attractive lake to the rear. The main public room,
incorporating bar, is a grand affair two storeys high, with a
wrought-iron gallery. Bedrooms come in a variety of sizes
and styles, much the best being 14 totally refurbished rooms
with stylish fabrics, good quality modern furniture and
sparkling new bathrooms; the rest are more old-fashioned,
though acceptable and clean, but in need of a face-lift.
Amenities garden, 24-hour lounge service, in-house movies,
games room, pool tables, table tennis.

HOTEL

Weybridge   Ship Thistle Hotel

£B/C
63%

Monument Green, Surrey. Weybridge
(0932) 48364 ● Map 10D3. Follow signs for
Chertsey and then Weybridge (A317).
Hotel is on left in town centre ● Bedrooms
39. En suite 39. With phone 39. With TV 39
● Confirm by 6 ● *Credit* Access, Amex,
Diners, Visa

This delightful town-centre hotel is kept in ship-shape
condition. The Transatlantic Bar with staff in smart navy
stewards' uniforms is most attractive, and the reception
lounge-cum-bar provides a cosy welcome. Walls here and
throughout the hotel continue the ship theme with prints of
old sailing vessels. Individually decorated bedrooms have
good darkwood furniture and pretty floral-print fabrics. All are
equipped with trouser presses, hairdryers and tea-makers.
In winter they are kept beautifully warm. Bathrooms offer a
nice range of toiletries. No dogs. *Amenities* 24-hour lounge
service, patio, restaurant (10am–11pm), in house movies,
laundry service.

Woking   Wheatsheaf Hotel

£E

Chobham Road, Surrey. Woking (048 62)
73047 ● Map 10C4. Follow signs for
Woking (A320). Take 4th exit off Six Cross
roundabout. Turn left at T-junction. Hotel is
on right ● Bedrooms 38. En suite 3. With
phone: some. With TV 38 ● Confirm by
arrangement ● *Credit* Access, Amex,
Diners, Visa

Situated opposite a cricket field not far from the town centre,
this is an unpretentious, brick-built inn providing modest
overnight accommodation, ideal for the business traveller on
a restricted budget. The reception area and convivial bar
were refurbished not long ago and have smart blue/grey
woodwork painted with grained effect. There's also a public
bar. Bedrooms in the original building are spacious and
traditionally furnished – bathrooms being a little old-fashioned.
Rooms in the new wing are compact (mostly singles), simply
furnished with modern units and smart, well-tiled, bathrooms.
All rooms offer colour TV, radio-alarms and tea-makers.

JUNCTION
–12–

EXIT SIGNS

Travelling
  clockwise

M3 Basingstoke
     Southampton
     Sunbury

Travelling
  anticlockwise

M3 Sunbury
     Basingstoke
     Southampton

HOTEL

Bagshot — Pennyhill Park Hotel

£C 76%

College Ride, Surrey. Bagshot (0276) 71774 ● Map 10B3. Take M3 west towards

Basingstoke. Exit at junction 3. Follow signs for Bracknell and Bagshot. At Bagshot take A30 towards Basingstoke. Turn right into Church Road ● Bedrooms 50. En suite 50. With phone 50. With TV 50 ● Confirm by arrangement ● *Credit* Access, Amex, Diners, Visa

Surrounded by lovely gardens and parkland, this splendid creeper-clad hotel makes an ideal choice for prestigious business meetings. Elegant public areas include a handsome lounge with fine oil paintings and a delightful conservatory. There are some impressive suites in the main house and a few of the rooms have antique furniture. Rooms in the new wing are particularly luxurious, with stylish Italian furniture and sumptuous bathrooms equipped with second TV and telephone. No dogs. *Amenities* garden, sauna, outdoor swimming pool, tennis, 9-hole golf course, game fishing, riding & stabling, helipad, clay-pigeon shooting, putting, table tennis, laundry service.

HOTEL

Camberley — Frimley Hall Hotel

£C/D 67%

Portsmouth Road, Surrey. Camberley (0276) 28231 ● Map 10A4. Take M3 west towards Basingstoke. Exit at junction 3. Follow signs for Bracknell and Bagshot. At Bagshot take A30 towards Basingstoke. Turn left onto A325 towards Farnborough ● Bedrooms 65. En suite 65. With phone 65. With TV 65 ● Confirm by arrangement ● *Credit* Access, Amex, Diners, Visa

This fine Victorian mansion, set in four acres of floodlit grounds, retains much of its original character and atmosphere. The lofty entrance hall features a beautiful carved oak staircase and gallery. Handsome gold-velour button-back chairs set an elegant tone in the lounge while oil paintings and a huge mirror continue this theme into the cocktail bar. Spacious bedrooms decorated in mellow creams and beige are smartly appointed with polished wood furniture; all have writing desks, occasional tables and side chairs. Tea-making equipment, magazines and tissues are provided. Bathrooms are fully tiled and have shower facilities.

Camberley   Tithas

31 High Street, Surrey. Camberley (0276)
23279 ● Map 10A4. Take M3 west towards
Basingstoke. Exit at junction 4, following
signs for Camberley town centre.
Restaurant is on right halfway down High
Street ● Lunch 12–2.30. Dinner 6–12 ● Set
L £3·95. About £26 for two ● *Credit*
Access, Amex, Diners, Visa ● Closed 25 &
26 December

Long and narrow, spick-and-span, this pleasant Indian
restaurant stands in the middle of Camberley's main shopping
street. The cooking is reliably good, throughout an appetising
range of tandoori dishes and curries, and there are various
chicken specialities. If you want to sample a well-balanced
variety of dishes, try a thali (set meal), either meat or
vegetarian. The meat thali features tender breast of marinated
tandoori chicken, spiced minted lamb sausage (seeka kebab),
mild lamb curry with peppers (rojan josh) and spicy roast
chicken pieces in a creamy pale orange sauce (murgh
makhami), plus rice, bread and vegetable side dishes.

Charlton Village   Harrow

(Food)

142 Charlton Road, Shepperton,
Middlesex. Sunbury (0932) 783122 ● Map
10D2. Take M3 to Sunbury. Follow signs
for Staines (A308) and then for Charlton
and Shepperton. Pub is on right in centre
of village ● *Brewery* Watney. *Beers*
Watney's Stag Bitter; Ben Truman;
Webster's Yorkshire Bitter; Guinness;
Carlsburg; Foster's

Reputedly the oldest inhabited building in Middlesex, this
lovely thatched cottage has a lot of charm and is worth visiting
for its curiosity value alone. Note especially the marvellous
open fireplaces built into the 16th-century stone walls. You'll
find the place busy at lunchtime, when crowds pack into the
low-beamed bars to enjoy the good food. A blackboard
announces familiar favourites like quiche, jacket potatoes,
shepherd's pie and a roast. Simple starters and sweets, plus
sandwiches (the sole Saturday choice). Patio and garden.
Typical prices: Shepherd's pie £2 Steak & kidney pie £2·75
(No bar food eves or Sun). ☺

RESTAURANT

Richmond   Caffe Mamma

124 Hill Street, Surrey. 01-940 1625 ● Map
10F1. Take M3 and then A316 towards
London. Follow signs for Richmond town
centre. Turn left into Hill Street ● Meals
noon–midnight ● About £16 for two ●
Credit Access, Amex, Visa ● Closed 25 &
26 December

Full marks for ingenuity go to this colourful Italian restaurant
for its imaginative decor. The effect is of an Italian street
scene, with fake shuttered windows on the walls, washing
strung high across the ceiling and pavement café furniture.
Fresh pasta is the food here. It comes al dente in all shapes
and sizes and deliciously sauced with anything from tuna and
green peppers to melted Gorgonzola. Fried squid or
minestrone for starters, and an interesting choice of well
presented salads like fennel, cucumber, orange and ricotta in
a herby dressing. Cakes and ice creams for dessert.

Richmond   Lichfield's

Sheen Road, Surrey. 01-940 5236 ● Map
10F1. On A305. Take M3 and then A316
towards London. Follow signs for
Richmond town centre. Turn left into
Sheen Road. Restaurant is on left ●
Lunch 12.15–2.30. Dinner 7–10.30 ● Set L
£14. Set D £15 & £20. About £50 for two ●
Credit Access, Amex ● Closed L Sat, all
Sun, Mon, Bank Holidays, 1st 2 weeks
September & 10 days Christmas

Careful, conscientious and highly skilled, owner-chef Stephen
Bull continues in top form at this smart, stylish restaurant in a
row of shops. The menus change daily to make use of the
best and freshest market produce, and the simple, mouth-
watering descriptions, often with brilliantly imaginative combinations, make the final choice a delightful problem. Recent
happy decisions include warm salad of calf's liver with
raspberry vinegar, venison with a timbale of Parma ham and
red cabbage, steamed hazelnut pudding in a wild strawberry
sauce. Presentation is superb. Attractive wines include Quarts
de Chaume dessert wine by the glass. ℮

Richmond   Mrs Beeton

58 Hill Rise, Surrey. 01-940 9561 ● Map
10F1. Off A307. Take M3 and then A316
towards London. Follow signs for
Richmond town centre. Turn left into Hill
Street. Restaurant is just up the hill on left
● Open 10–5 (Sun from 11), also 6.30–11
Wed–Sat. Closed 1 week Christmas

Every day brings somethings new in this popular restaurant,
where pairs of local ladies work in rotation. Atmosphere is
relaxed and informal, with tables on the pavement outside in
summer. A recent visit found the kitchen in the capable hands
of Maureen Slaven and Jo Pettman, whose menu ranged
from pork and thyme pâte with stoneground bread to tasty
tuna gratin, courgette roulade and blanquette of lamb. Cakes
and sweets included lemon tart and a lovely brown sugar
meringue of chocolate, coffee and cream. Unlicensed – bring
your own. No dogs. *Typical prices:* Courgette roulade £2·70
Mexican gâteau 85p. WC

Richmond   Petersham Hotel

£D
62%

Nightingale Lane, Richmond Hill, Surrey.
01-940 7471 ● Map 10F1. Take M3 and
then A316 to Richmond. Follow signs for
Kingston. Bear right at the fork. Take the
low road and follow signs for Nightingale
Lane. Hotel is signposted ● Bedrooms 56.
En suite 56. With phone 56. With TV 56 ●
Confirm by 6 ● *Credit* Access, Amex,
Diners, Visa

Commanding splendid views over the Thames, this is a
handsome Victorian hotel that has recently been extensively
refurbished. The spacious foyer features a fine Portland
stone staircase and lofty ceiling painting. The lounge is more
cosy and intimate, with comfortable leather chesterfields,
while the modern bar provides a sense of place with prints of
famous people connected with Richmond. Nine of the larger
bedrooms have river views as well as superior, period-style
furnishings and bigger bathrooms. Elsewhere bedrooms are
bright and modern, all with hairdryers and tea-makers.
Friendly, courteous staff. No dogs. *Amenities* garden, dancing
(Fri, Sat), laundry service.

JUST A BITE

Richmond   Refectory

6 Church Walk, Surrey. 01-940 6264 ●
Map 10F1. Off A305. Take M3 and then
A316 towards London. Follow signs for
Richmond town centre. Turn immediate
left into Church Road, right into Sheen
Road and bear left at fork (Paradise Rd).
Turn right at the church. ● Open 10–2 also
Thurs–Sat 7.30–10.30 (last orders 8.45).
Sun noon–2.15. Closed Mon, Bank
Holidays & 8 days Christmas.

Tucked away in the old church rooms, with a nice little courtyard for summer eating, this restaurant starts the day at a civilized hour by serving mid-morning coffee. A tasty lunchtime menu soone takes over (minimum charge £1·50) and always features some vegetarian food. Dishes range from home-made granary bread with potted meats, smoked mackerel pâte and savoury flans to specials like cheese-topped cottage pie, nut loaf and lamb casserole. Interesting vegetables, and pleasant sweets such as apricot fool or chocolate cream pudding. Evening menu is more ambitious. *Typical prices;* Lamb casserole £2·75 Chocolate cream pudding £1·45. ● WC

HOTEL

Richmond   Richmond Gate Hotel

£D
60%

Richmond Hill, Surrey. 01-940 0061 ● Map
10F1. See Petersham Hotel (page 105) for
directions ● Bedrooms 50. En suite 50.
With phone 50 ● With TV 50 ● Confirm by 6
● *Credit* Access, Amex, Diners, Visa

An attractive Georgian hotel, sister and neighbour of the Petersham. The lounge is decorated with old prints of Richmond and has traditional though rather tired-looking furnishings. The bar is much smarter and conveys a pleasantly cosy atmosphere. Most of the bedrooms are in a modern block behind the main building. They are simply but attractively decorated with good quality fabrics. Bathrooms are fully tiled and compact. Five larger bedrooms in the main building (three with four-posters) are better appointed and have bigger bathrooms. Bed and breakfast only (meals may be taken at the Petersham). No dogs. *Amenities* garden, laundry service.

Richmond   Richmond Harvest

5 Dome Buildings, The Quadrant, Surrey.
01-940 1138 ● Map 10F1. Off A305. Take
M3 and then A316 towards London. Follow
signs for Richmond town centre.

Restaurant is on left on the corner of
Sheen Road and the Quadrant ● Open
11.30–11 (Sun till 10.30). Closed 25
December–1 January

A tiny vegetarian restaurant in the centre of town, with close-packed tables, cheery staff and a devoted clientele. The ever-changing selection of home-prepared fare (new menus twice daily) includes plenty of vegan dishes. Everything is commendably fresh and wholesome, from piping hot barley and vegetable soup to crunchy salads and main courses such as courgette casserole with olives, tomatoes, black-eyed beans and plenty of garlic. Excellent puds like hot fruit crumble, and there are cakes for afternoon coffee. Minimum charge £1·95. No dogs. *Typical prices:* Mediterranean courgette casserole £3·15 Cheese & vegetable pie £1·85. WC

Richmond   Wildefoods Wholefood Café

98 Kew Road, Surrey. 01-940 0733 ● Map
10F1. Take M3 and then A316 towards
London. Turn left into Kew Road (1st exit
off Richmond roundabout). Café is 200
yards down on right ● Open 9–7, Sun
noon–5. Closed Sun in winter, 1 January,
Good Fri, 25 & 26 December & 1 week
summer

A few tables in a vegetarian wholefood shop and takeaway. Items available to eat on the spot might include samosas, a couple of quiches. Gruyère and watercress pie and lentil burgers. All can be heated (in a microwave) if you prefer. There are also decent salads, plus baps, sandwiches, jacket potatoes and all sorts of cakes and pastries like carrot cake and apricot almond slice. Organically grown vegetables are widely used. Preparation is something of a cottage industry, with contributions from various local sources. Unlicensed. No smoking. No dogs. *Typical prices:* Cheese & lentil bake 40p Date slice 25p. ✆

HOTEL

Shepperton   Shepperton Moat House

£D
60%

Felix Lane, Middlesex. Walton-on-Thames (0932) 241404 ● Map 10D3. Follow signs for Sunbury (M3 to junction 1), then for Lower Sunbury. Turn right onto B375 signposted Chertsey ● Bedrooms 180. En suite 180. With phone 180. With TV180 ● Confirm by 6 ● *Credit* Access, Amex, Diners, Visa

A modern low-rise hotel peacefully situated near the Thames yet handy for the motorway network and Heathrow. There is a bright and airy open-plan reception area with bar and plenty of comfortable seating. Elsewhere a programme of refurbishment has been underway and all of the bedrooms have been freshly and attractively decorated and offer remote-control TVs with radio, direct-dial phones and tea-makers. Bathrooms are functional but adequate. *Amenities* garden, sauna, keep-fit equipment, target golf, dinner dance (Sat), helipad, in-house movies, landing stage, laundry service, children's play area, snooker, pool table, 24-hour lounge service.

RESTAURANT

Sunbury-on-Thames   Castle

21 Thames Street, Middlesex. Sunbury-on-Thames (093 27) 83647 ● Map 10E2. Follow signs for Sunbury (M3 to junction 1), then for Lower Sunbury. Turn left into Thames Street ● Lunch 12–2.30. Dinner 7–10 ● Set L & D from £11·20. About £40 for two ● *Credit* Access, Amex, Diners, Visa ● Closed L Sat, all Sun, Bank Holidays, 1 week Easter, 1 week August & 1 week Christmas

Elegant surroundings, careful cooking and impeccable service create a sense of well-being at this civilised restaurant. Owner-chef Giuseppe Mele comes from north-east Italy, near the Austrian border, but specialises in French classical and regional dishes. His cuisine is both imaginative and assured but refreshingly free from gimmicks and pointless showmanship. Appetising choices range from crab and lobster soup and prawns with Pernod to carré d'agneau and seasonal game – both seafood and game are something of a speciality here. Nicely cooked vegetables. Sorbets, fruit brûlés and crêpes feature among the tempting desserts. ♀ *WELL-CHOSEN* house wine.

Twickenham   Prince Albert

(Food)

30 Hampton Road, Middlesex. 01-894
3963 ● Map 10E2. Take M3 to Sunbury,
then A316. Follow signs for Teddington at
first roundabout, turning into Hospital
Bridge Road. Turn left at second set of
traffic lights. Pub is 500 yards down on left
● *Brewery* Fuller's. *Beers* Fuller's
Chiswick Bitter, ESB Bitter, London Pride;
Guinness; Heineken; Tennent's Extra

A really delightful Victorian pub, with affable staff, excellent food and a real feeling of *rus in urbe.* Elizabeth Lunn puts a lot of time and thought into her lunchtime menus. Begin with a tempting starter such as mussels bretonne or tuna fish crumble, then choose from main-course delights as diverse as salmon trout, Spanish scrambled egg, seafood grill, liver and bacon, steak pie and tasty pork casserole with wine and mushrooms. Pancakes are a popular pud. Toasted sandwiches are the only evening choice. Patio and garden. *Typical prices:* Seafood grill £6 Pork in fine herbs £3·50 (no bar food Sun). ☺

Twickenham   White Swan

(Food)

Riverside, Middlesex. 01-892 2166 ● Map
10E2. Take M3 to Sunbury. Follow signs
for Twickenham and Richmond (A316 &
A305). Bear right at road fork into Church
Lane. Take first right, then first left into
Riverside ● Last bar food 10.30pm ●
Brewery Watney Combe Reid. *Beers*
Watney's Special Bitter; Combes Bitter;
Webster's Yorkshire Bitter; Guinness;
Carlsberg; Foster's; cider

A friendly pub with a small terrace and garden that takes full advantage of the riverside setting. Eat here or in the homely bar where, from about 1 o'clock, Shirley Sutton's freshly prepared snacks are served. Typical offerings might include a creamy courgette and potato soup, pâté, quiche, ploughman's, cannelloni, beef hot pot, pork chops in cider and a vegetarian special like grilled avocado and Stilton salad. Nice sweet pastries to follow, like French apple tart. Rolls and sandwiches only in the evening. Children welcome lunchtime. *Typical prices:* Beef hot pot £2.60 Home-made soup £1·20. No bar food Sun). ☺

JUNCTION –13–

EXIT SIGNS

Travelling clockwise	A30	London (W) Staines
Travelling anticlockwise	A30	Staines

HOTEL

Ascot   **Berystede Hotel**

£C
68%

Bagshot Road, Sunninghill, Berkshire.
Ascot (0990) 23311 ● Map 10B3. Take A30
towards Basingstoke and follow signs for
Ascot/Bracknell on B329. Turn off onto
B3020 towards Sunninghill ● Bedrooms
92. En suite 92. With phone 92. With TV 92
● Confirm by 6 ● *Credit* Access, Amex,
Diners, Visa

A turreted Victorian house at the heart of this well-run hotel,
whose elegant foyer-lounge features a fine oak staircase and
an elaborate gilt chandelier. There's also a relaxing bar with
comfortable settees, paintings of racehorses and views over
the lawns. Bedrooms are smart, stylish and well equipped,
those in the main house with separate sitting areas being
particularly desirable. All rooms have good modern bathrooms. Pleasant staff include neatly uniformed page boys.
Amenities garden, outdoor swimming pool, putting, croquet,
golf driving net, games room, table tennis, pool table, dinner
dance (Sat), 24-hour lounge service, laundry service, in-
house movies.

Ascot — Royal Berkshire

£B 76%

London Road, Sunninghill,
Berkshire. Ascot (0990)
23322 ● Map 10B3. Take
A30 (Egham) for approx. 4
miles. Then take A329
towards Ascot ● Bedrooms
40. En suite 40. With phone
40. With TV 40 ● Confirm by 6 ● *Credit* Access, Amex,
Diners, Visa

Standings in 15 acres of grounds, this handsome Queen Anne mansion has been splendidly restored and discreetly modernised. Period proportions and stylish contemporary fabrics blend harmoniously in the public rooms, where the original panelling is now most effectively stained a light blue-grey. The same colour is equally attractive in the spacious bedrooms, where an impressive range of accessories includes hairdryers, trouser presses, mini-bars, stationery and remote-control TVs. Bathrooms too, are very well appointed. Excellent service from general manager Robin Shepperd and a friendly, attentive team. *Amenities* garden, sauna, tennis, squash, croquet, helipad, putting, laundry service.

Ascot — Royal Berkshire Restaurant

London Road, Sunninghill, Berkshire.
Ascot (0990) 23322 ● Map 10B3. See hotel
entry above for directions ● Lunch 12.30–
2. Dinner 7.30–9.30 ● Set L £13·50. Set D
£19.50. About £55 for two ● *Credit* Access,
Amex, Diners, Visa

This chic hotel restaurant, set in an elegantly proportioned Queen Anne room overlooking the garden, is a stylish blend of old and new. The old pine panelling is stained a smart, contemporary grey-blue and there are modern touches in the beautifully designed glass and tableware. Chef Jonathan Fraser echoes this theme of old and new, bringing a bold fresh modernity to classic skills. His artistry is illustrated in dishes like impeccably light ravioli of turbot with caviar butter, caramelised duck breast with a Sauternes-based sauce or rhubarb pudding with pastis. Excellent English cheeses. Service friendly and informed. ♀ *WELL-CHOSEN* house wine. ⊖

Ascot   Stag

(Food)

63 High Street, Berkshire, Ascot (0990)
21622 ● Map 10B3. Take A30 towards
Basingstoke and follow signs for Ascot/
Bracknell on B329. Pub is on left of High
Street, opposite shopping precinct ● Last
bar food 10pm ● *Brewery* Friary Meux.
Beers Friary Meux Traditional Bitter; John
Bull Bitter; Guinness; Castlemaine 4X;
Skol; cider

Home-made wholemeal pasta is just one of many good things
produced by Ann McCarthy in this friendly high-street pub,
where racing prints and photographs recall the close proximity
of Ascot race course. Filled jacket potatoes are another
popular choice, along with burgers, salads, made-to-order
sandwiches and specials like fried haddock or chicken and
ham pie. To round off a tasty, wholesome meal there are
homely sweets like apple and cherry crumble. Organically-
grown vegetables used whenever possible. Pavement tables.
Children welcome. *Typical prices:* Chicken & ham pie £2·30
Vegetable lasagne £2 (Limited choice Sun).

Ashford   Terrazza

45 Church Road, Middlesex. Ashford (078
42) 44887 ● Map 10D2. Follow signs for
London West (A30), then for Ashford. Turn
right at crossroads by the hospital into
Stanwell Road. Restaurant is just beyond
railway station ● Lunch 12–2.30. Dinner 7–
10.30 ● Set L & D £10·75 incl. wine. About
£45 for two ● *Credit* Access, Amex,
Diners, Visa ● Closed L Sat, all Sun &
Bank Holidays

Personal attention from the owners is a nice feature of this
neat, popular Italian restaurant in Ashford's main shopping
street. Deftly-manoeuvred trolleys play a major role here,
bearing a mouth-watering display of antipasti and a fine
selection of seafood including salmon and lobster. The à la
carte menu provides plenty of variety, from excellent spagh-
ettini al pesto to scampi all diavola, chicken sorpresa, veal
chops with sage and steaks from the grill. Cooking is reliably
good, with robust flavours and generous portions. Diners will
find it hard to resist the tempting sweet trolley, especially the
rich chocolate mousse gâteau.

Egham   Great Fosters

£C/D 70%

Stroude Road,
Surrey. Egham
(0784) 33822 ●
Map 10C2.
Follow signs
Egham Town.

Keep left on one-way system towards railway station. Hotel is just beyond station ● Bedrooms 44. En suite 44. With phone 44. With TV 44 ● Confirm by arrangement ● *Credit* Access, Amex, Diners, Visa

Once a royal hunting lodge, this mellow building enjoys a favoured setting in lovely gardens. The hall, with its oak panelling, ornate plasterwork ceiling and Jacobean fireplace, is quite magnificent, and there's a comfortable lounge as well as a beamed bar. The 15th-century tithe barn is a superb venue for dances. Some of the bedrooms in the main house have wall tapestries and handsome antiques; two feature four-posters. In the stable-block conference centre there are modern single bedrooms. No dogs. *Amenities* garden, outdoor swimming pool, sauna, table tennis, dinner dance (Sat), 24-hour lounge service.

Egham   Runnymede Hotel

£C/D 70%

Windsor Road,
Surrey. Egham
(0784) 36171 ●
Map 10C2.
Take A308 for
Windsor. Hotel

is on right ● Bedrooms 124. En suite 124. With phone 124. With TV 124 ● Confirm by 6 ● *Credit* Access, Amex, Diners, Visa

Standards of service are high at this smooth-running, modern red-brick hotel. The accent is on light and comfort in the foyer-lounge, where picture windows look out across the terrace to the Thames. There is an attractive cocktail bar and a choice of function/conference suites. Bedrooms are decorated and furnished in pleasant, up-to-date style, with all the usual accessories and roomy, sparkling bathrooms. Executive rooms in a separate wing feature individually controlled air conditioning. *Amenities* garden, coarse fishing, helipad, dinner dance (Sat), jazz (Mon, Thurs), in-house movies, 24-hour lounge service, laundry service.

JUNCTIONS
14–16

JUNCTION
–15–

EXIT SIGNS

Travelling clockwise	M4	The West Slough London W Heathrow terminals 1, 2 & 3, $3\frac{1}{2}$
Travelling anticlockwise	M4	London W Heathrow terminals 1, 2 & 3, $3\frac{1}{2}$ The West Slough

Bray	**Crown Inn**

(Food)

High Street, Berkshire. Maidenhead (0628) 36725 ● Map 9B3. Take M4 towards The West. Exit at junction 8/9. Follow signs for Maidenhead centre. At next roundabout follow signs for Bray ● *Credit* Access, Amex ● *Brewery* Courage. *Beers* Courage Best Bitter; Guinness; Hofmeister; Kronenbourg

Right in the centre of Bray, opposite the village hall, this attractive old inn offers tasty lunchtime bar snacks in a delightfully traditional setting. Friendly bar staff and blazing open fires in winter add a welcoming touch. Highlights of the changing blackboard menu include pâté, roast lamb, cottage pie and lovely home-made flans like prawn and tomato, with a splendid treacle tart for afters. On Saturday filled rolls only, and a barbecue in the garden for Sunday lunch (if fine). Patio. Children welcome. *Typical prices:* Steak & mushroom pie £3·20 Cheese & asparagus pie £2·85 (No bar food eves). ℗

PUB

Bray-on-Thames   Monkey Island Hotel

£C/D
60%

Near Maidenhead, Berkshire. Maidenhead
(0628) 23400 ● Map 9B3. Take M4
towards The West. Exit at junction 8/9.
Follow signs for Maidenhead Centre, then
take A308 towards Windsor for $\frac{1}{4}$ mile.
Turn left for Bray ● Bedrooms 26. En suite
26. With phone 26. With TV 26 ● Confirm
by arrangement ● *Credit* Access, Amex,
Diners, Visa ● Closed 25 & 26 December

Monkey Island, reached by a foot suspension bridge, is a peaceful place of splendid lawns and trees, set in the Thames about a mile downstream from Maidenhead. The hotel is equally delightful. A former fishing lodge houses the large bar and the fascinating Monkey Room with its 18th-century mural of monkeys in period costume. Accommodation, along with reception, a residents' lounge and a fine octagonal function room, is in another building a short walk from the lodge. A major refurbishment programme is under-way, and the bedrooms are to be redecorated in attractive country style. No dogs. *Amenities* garden, coarse fishing, dinner dance (monthly), jetty.

Bray-on-Thames   Waterside Inn

★★

Ferry Road, Berkshire. Maidenhead (0628)
20691 ● Map 9B3. Take M4 towards The
West. Exit at junction 8/9. Take A308(M)
and follow signs to Bray ● Lunch 12–2,
Sun 12–2.30. Dinner 7–10 ● Set L from
£19·50. Set D £35. About £100 for two ●
Credit Access, Amex, Diners, Visa ●
Closed Mon, L Tues, also D Sun October–
Easter, Bank Holidays & 25 December–
end January (except L 25 December)

The magical riverside setting and the renown of Michel Roux raise expectations sky high at this beautifully appointed restaurant. Just occasionally, especially on a day when Michel is not in the kitchen, the spark of sheer brilliance fades and little lapses can occur. Most dishes, however, remain unqualified creative triumphs, well conceived and deftly executed. Service is certainly sophisticated – finger bowls, fresh napkins after the main course, warmed coffee cups – but can lack the human touch. *Specialities* cassolette d'écrevisses et fruits de mer aux tagliatelles á l'huile de crustacés, rognon de veau rôti dans sa graisse aux deux poivres. ▱ *OUTSTANDING.* ⊖

HOTEL

Burnham · Grovefield Hotel

£D
63%

Taplow Common Road, Buckinghamshire. Burnham (062 86) 3131 ● Map 9B3. Take M4 towards The West. Exit at junction 7. Take A4 towards Maidenhead. Turn right for Lent Rise ● Bedrooms 33. En suite 33. With phone 33. With TV 33 ● Confirm by arrangement ● *Credit* Access, Amex, Diners, Visa

This red-brick hotel enjoys a secluded location in seven acres of grounds. The building was skilfully extended in 1984, repeating the style of the original to ensure visual continuity. At the same time the interior was smartly redesigned. A bright, spacious bar-lounge furnished in cane leads off the foyer and there's a small residents' lounge. Roomy bedrooms include ground-floor garden rooms approached via patio doors from the outside. All have simple darkwood units and a pleasantly unfussy decor. Tea-makers are standard. Bathrooms are modern, carpeted and with coloured units. *Amenities* garden, croquet.

Cranford · Berkeley Arms Hotel

£C/D
65%

Bath Road, Middlesex. 01-897 2121 ● Map 9E3. Take M4 towards London West. Exit at junction 3. Follow signs for Heathrow (A312). Take 3rd exit off next roundabout into Bath Road. Hotel is on right ● Bedrooms 40, En suite 40. With phone 40. With TV 40 ● Confirm by 6 ● *Credit* Access, Amex, Diners, Visa

Two miles east of airport, this well-run hotel with an attractive garden has had its public rooms completely revamped. Soft pastel shades – ice blue, petal pink, dove grey – predominate, with plants, flower arrangements and bamboo furniture contributing to a feel of cool, contemporary elegance. Bar, lounge and foyer together form a spacious open-plan living area. Bedrooms are both pleasant and practical with colourful woollen bedcovers, built-in white units, two armchairs apiece, hairdryers, tea-makers, direct-dial phones and remote-control TVs. Well-fitted bathrooms, all with shower facilities, shampoo and bath foam. *Amenities* garden, transport to airport.

HOTEL

117

PUB

Dorney — Palmer Arms

(Food)

Village Road, Near Windsor, Buckinghamshire. Burnham (062 86) 66612 ● Map 9B3. Take M4 towards The West. Exit at junction 7. Follow signs for Slough, then Maidenhead (A4). Turn onto B3026 signposted Dorney. Pub is on left ● Last bar food 10pm ● *Credit* Access, Visa ● *Brewery* Regent Inns. *Beers* Bass Bitter, Charrington IPA, Toby Bitter; M&B Mild; Guinness; Carling Black Label; Tennent's Extra; cider

Stylishly revamped, this friendly village pub offers enjoyable food in its smart pine-clad bar. Starters and snacks might include a creamy lettuce soup and tasty duck and orange terrine. Follow, perhaps, with minty grilled lamb cutlets or sautéed fillet of beef in a rich red-wine sauce. Or, if fish is your dish, try a seafood special like crab-claw salad or lemon sole in a shrimp and mushroom sauce. Fresh fruits with liqueurs make a delicious finale. Speedy, pleasant service. Garden. Children welcome. *Typical prices:* Chicken suprême in avocado & garlic sauce £3·95 Sirloin steak with herb butter £5·25.

HOTEL

Eton — Christopher Hotel

£E
(B&B)

High Street, Near Windsor, Berkshire. Windsor (0753) 852359 ● Map 9C3. Take M4 towards The West. Exit at junction 6. Follow signs for Eton. Hotel is in town centre on right of High Street ● Bedrooms 21. With bath/shower 21. With TV 21 ● Check-in all day ● *Credit* Access, Amex, Diners, Visa ● Free House. *Beers* Brakspear Bitter; John Smith's Bitter; Courage Best Bitter; Younger's Tartan; Guinness; Hofmeister; Kronenbourg; cider

Look for the archway between the Christopher Bar and Peacock Bar and you'll see your way to the hotel entrance, which is set slightly off the High Street. Good-sized bedrooms (mostly in a block adjoining the main building) offer comfortable overnight accommodation plus useful extras like hairdryers, trouser presses and fridges (with makings of a continental breakfast). Six larger bedrooms are arranged as family rooms, with bunk beds for children. All rooms have pay telephones. Christopher Bar is Victorian in style with nice pubby atmosphere; Peacock Bar is smarter and more intimate, the perfect place for a quiet drink. Terrace.

Eton · Eton Wine Bar

82 High Street, Berkshire. Windsor (0753)
854921 ● Map 9C3. Take M4 towards The
West. Exit at junction 6. Follow signs for
Eton. Wine bar is in town centre on right ●
Open noon–2.30 & 6–11, Sun noon–2 & 7–
10. Closed Easter Sun & 3–4 days
Christmas ● *Credit* Access, Visa

The blackboard menu in this neat, pine-furnished wine bar
shows a short selection of imaginative, carefully prepared
dishes. Smoked salmon mousse and soups like cauliflower
and cress or cucumber and mint are typical starters, preceding
main courses like chicken, ham and pepper cocotte. Nice
sweets, too, perhaps including a pleasantly tart summer
pudding or a chilled nectarine, brandy and raspberry soufflé.
Menu changes frequently, justifying the narrow choice, and
there is an especially good house wine. Friendly, informal
atmosphere. No smoking. No dogs. *Typical prices:* Chicken,
ham & pepper cocotte £4·25 Veal & almond casserole with
turmeric rice £4·75. ⊛ WC

Hayes · Ariel Hotel

£C
65%

Bath Road, Middlesex. 01-759 2552 ● Map
9E3. Follow signs for Heathrow (M4). Turn
left into Bath Rd (A4). Hotel is on left ●
Bedrooms 177. En suite 177. With phone
177. With TV 177 ● Confirm by 6 ● *Credit*
Access, Amex, Diners, Visa.

This distinctive circular hotel is conveniently located only 2
miles from Heathrow airport. Its focal point is the central
patio, attractively filled with flowering plants and shrubs. An
ornamental fountain in the lounge area continues the relaxing
garden theme as does the stylish Oasis cocktail bar. Most of
the bedrooms have now been totally refurbished and have
direct-dial phones and remote-control TVs. Bathrooms are
modern and well-equipped, with plenty of extras. Friendly,
helpful staff prove that airport hotels need not be impersonal.
Amenities 24-hour lounge service, transport for airport, in-
house movies, laundry service, kiosk.

HOTEL

Hayes   Sheraton Skyline

£A/B 77%

Bath Road. Middlesex. 01-759 2535 ● Map 9E3. Follow signs for Heathrow (M4). Turn left into

Bath Road (A4). Hotel is on left ● Bedrooms 355. En suite 355. With phone 355. With TV 355 ● Confirm by 4 ● *Credit* Access, Amex, Diners, Visa

Near the entrance to Heathrow airport, this fine modern hotel is centred around an indoor tropical garden complete with swimming pool and lounge bar. Other public areas cater for various moods: Diamond Lil's Saloon stages a six-nights-a-week cabaret, while the Edwardian-style cocktail bar is a popular spot for a quieter drink. Bedrooms offer space, style and comfort, with good-quality furnishings, double glazing, air conditioning and excellent bathrooms. *Amenities* patio, sauna, indoor swimming pool, solarium, in-house movies, cabaret (Mon–Sat), beauty salon, hairdressing, shopping arcade, transport for airport and central London, coffee shop (6am–1am).

RESTAURANT

Hayes   Sheraton Skyline, Colony Room

Bath Road, Middlesex. 01-759 2535 ● Map 9E3. See hotel entry above for directions ● Lunch 12.30–2.30. Dinner 7–11, Fri & Sat 7–11.30 ● Set L £15·95. About £60 for two ● *Credit* Access, Amex, Diners, Visa ● Closed L Sat & Sun, also all lunches in August

Skilled French cooking and polished, professional service in comfortable, elegant surroundings. The evening menu offers a wealth of choice and might include starters like guinea hen and sweetbread terrine or watercress and spinach soup served with delicate fish quenelles. To follow there might be breast of duck with mango or salmon en croûte with a delicious gingery beurre blanc. Good variety of vegetables, though over-salting can be a problem here. Trolley sweets, plus ices, crêpes and a vast selection of cheeses. Evening menu changes every few months but is regularly adjusted to include seasonal produce. Lunchtime table d'hôte also seasonal.

Hayes — Skyway Hotel

£C/D
63%

Bath Road, Middlesex. 01-759 6311 ● Map
9E3. Follow signs for Heathrow (M4). Turn
left into Bath Road (A4). Hotel is on left ●
Bedrooms 412. En suite 412. With phone
412. With TV 412 ● Confirm by 6 ● *Credit*
Access, Amex, Diners, Visa

Staff are friendly and welcoming at this purpose-built 1950s
hotel about a mile from Heathrow airport. There's a smart,
open-plan lounge and a bar whose decor features weekly-
changing themes ('New York', for example). Improvements
are well underway in the bedrooms. Most now have practical
modern units, tea-makers and direct-dial phones. Superior
rooms offer extras like air conditioning, trouser presses,
hairdryers and bathtime luxuries. All rooms are well sound-
proofed against aircraft noise. No dogs. *Amenities* outdoor
swimming pool, whirlpool bath, coffee shop (10am–midnight),
transport for airport, hairdressing, snooker, games room, in-
house movies, valeting, laundry room.

Hounslow — Heathrow Penta Hotel

£B/C 71%

Bath Road,
Middlesex. 01-
897 6363 ● Map
9E4. Follow
signs for
Heathrow (M4).
Hotel is situated

within the airport boundary ● Bedrooms 670. En suite 670.
With phone 670. With TV 670 ● Confirm by 6 ● *Credit*
Access, Amex, Diners, Visa

This striking modern hotel stands within the airport boundary,
and there are runway views from many rooms. Double-glazed
bedrooms, well equipped with the traveller in mind, are
stylishly designed, with high-quality furnishings and mini-
bars; up-to-date bathrooms are kept in excellent order. The
vast open-plan foyer-lounge has plenty of deep, comfortable
armchairs, while drinks are available in the Flying Machine
Bar or the cosy Drake's Bar. There's also an arcade of shops
and a cheerful coffee shop. Impressive leisure and function
facilities. *Amenities* sauna, indoor swimming pool, hairdressing, in-house movies, gymnasium, solarium, coffee-shop (24
hours), valeting, transport for airport, 24-hour lounge service.

HOTEL

Hounslow — Master Robert Motel

£D/E
59%

366 Great West Road, Middlesex. 01-570
6261 ● Map 9E4. Follow signs for London
West (M4). Exit at junction 3 and follow
signs for Hounslow (A4). Motel is a mile
down A4 on left ● Bedrooms 63. En suite
63. With phone 63. With TV 63 ● Confirm
by 6 ● *Credit* Access, Amex, Diners, Visa

This 1920s pub, named after the winner of the 1924 Grand National, was one of the first motels in Britain. Now modernised and with fresh improvements currently underway, it offers spacious accommodation close to Heathrow airport – either in the Lord Airlie wing (he owned the horse) or in chalet-style rooms. Older rooms are solidly furnished, though well-equipped with radios and tea-makers, and have plainly-fitted bathrooms. New-style rooms offer brighter fabrics and extras like hairdryers and trouser presses. There's a colourful, pine-furnished lounge bar and more traditional public bar. *Amenities* garden, transport for airport, lounge service (7.30am–11.30pm), Prestel.

JUST A BITE

Kew — Original Maids of Honour

★

288 Kew Road, Surrey. 01-940 2752 ●
Map 9F3. Take M4 towards London West.
Exit at junction 1. Take South Circular
(A205) to Kew. Tea shop is on left, about ½
mile beyond Kew Bridge ● Open 10–5.30
(Mon till 1). Closed Sun & Bank Holidays

In the Newens family for well over 100 years, this renowned temple of traditional baking has a reputation that is almost worldwide. Certainly it stands in a class of its own when compared with other pâtisseries in this country. The range and quality of the produce are quite outstanding, the artistry and perfectionism breathtaking, and nothing will leave you indifferent, from the legendary Maids of Honour to cream slices, crunchy brandy snaps and marvellous mille-feuilles. Equally impressive are savoury delights like sausage rolls and steak pies. No dogs. *Typical prices:* Maid of Honour 60p Set afternoon tea £2·25. WC

Kew   Pissarro's (Wine Bar)

1 Kew Green, Surrey. 01-940 3987 ● Map
9F3. Take M4 towards London West. Exit
at junction 1. Take South Circular (A205)
towards Kew. Kew Green is second
turning on right after Kew Bridge ● Open
11.30–2.30 & 7–10.30, Sun noon–2 & 7–10.
Closed Easter Sun & Mon & 25 & 26
December

Ancient beams and rustic tables and chairs create an old-world atmosphere at this attractive wine bar. The day's bill of fare, chalked up on a blackboard, might include smoked mackerel mousse or a thick, well-flavoured minestrone to start with, followed by beef bourguignon, lobster-sauced seafood with rice, chilli con carne, lasagne, entrecôte steak or roast lamb. The cold buffet is a popular alternative, with plenty of salads, and there's a good variety of sweets both bought-in and home-made, such as chocolate mousse. No children. *Typical prices:* Salmon mousse £1·70 Calf's liver with sage £5. WC

Kew   Wine & Mousaka

12 Kew Green, Surrey. 01-940 5696 ● Map
9F3. Take M4 towards London West. Exit
at junction 1. Take South Circular (A205)
towards Kew. Kew Green is second
turning on right after Kew Bridge ● Lunch
12–2.30. Dinner 6–11.30 ● About £18 for
two ● *Credit* Access, Amex, Diners, Visa ●
Closed Sun, Bank Holidays & 3 days
Christmas

Aromas of oregano and the charcoal grill will remind you of Greek holidays at this friendly restaurant overlooking Kew Green. The menu is nicely varied, with taramasalata, houmus, tsatsiki (minty cucumber and yogurt dip), stuffed peppers and vine leaves, calamari, moussaka and kebabs among the favourites. Meze, a chef's selection for two people, is well worth trying. So is the soutsoukakia – minced lamb well seasoned with garlic and cumin, rolled into sausages, grilled over charcoal and served with a garlicky tomato sauce. Cooking here is above average for a Greek restaurant, with real care taken over preparation and flavourings. Booking advisable.

HOTEL

Maidenhead   Crest Hotel

Manor Lane, Berkshire. Maidenhead
(0628) 23444 ● Map 9A3. Take M4
towards The West. Exit at junction 8/9.
Follow signs for Maidenhead West. Turn
off for Cox's Green/White Waltham and
then turn left at the T-junction ● Bedrooms
189. En suite 189. With phone 189. With TV
189 ● Confirm by 6 ● *Credit* Access,
Amex, Diners, Visa

£C
66%

Plenty of plants and greenery contribute to the relaxing
ambience of this newly-refurbished modern hotel. Public
areas are bright and airy and there's an attractive coffee shop
overlooking the new indoor pool. Standard bedrooms offer
direct-dial phones, radio-alarms and smart, well-fitted bathrooms. Executive rooms have mini-bars and are generally
larger and more stylish; those designated 'Lady Crest' offer
pretty, more feminine colour schemes plus extras such as
magazines. *Amenities* garden, indoor swimming pool, keep-
fit equipment, sauna, solarium, whirlpool bath, squash,
snooker, pool table, children's play area, in-house movies,
coffee shop (7am–11pm), 24-hour lounge service.

HOTEL

Maidenhead   Frederick's Hotel

£C 79%

Shoppenhangers
Road, Berkshire.
Maidenhead
(0628) 35934 ●
Map 9A3. Take
M4 towards

The West. Exit at junction 8/9. Follow signs for Maidenhead
West. Turn off for Cox's Green/White Waltham and then
follow signs again for Maidenhead ● Bedrooms 37. En suite
37. With phone 37. With TV 37 ● Confirm by arrangement ●
Credit Access, Amex, Diners, Visa

In a quiet residential area, this red-brick hotel offers
impressively high standards of comfort and service. Entrance
is into a splendid new foyer-lounge where classical busts and
plotted plants combine with stylish furnishings to create a
most elegant ambience. New, too, is the lovely conservatory,
and there's also plenty of room to relax in the spacious bar.
Immaculate bedrooms have comfortable, traditional furnishings, mini-bars and remote-control TVs. Most rooms in the
wing have video recorders. Bathrooms are equipped with
hairdryers, weighing scales and a good supply of towels. No
dogs. *Amenities* garden, in-house movies, laundry service.

Maidenhead   Fredrick's Hotel Restaurant

★

Shoppenhangers Road, Berkshire.
Maidenhead (0628) 24737 ● Map 9A3. See
hotel entry for directions ● Lunch 12–2.
Dinner 7–9.45 ● Set L £18·50. Set D
£25·50. About £60 for two ● *Credit* Access,
Amex, Diners, Visa ● Closed L Sat & all
26–30 December

Chris Cleveland has been at this elegant modern restaurant
for seven years, producing superb meals from tip-top raw
materials. His skills shine through dishes both simple and
elaborate – whether potage cressonnière bursting with the
clear, fresh flavour of watercress or fillet of lamb with a silky
Madeira sauce, garnished with sliced lamb's tongue and
artichokes filled with creamed leeks. Outstanding vegetables,
super sweet trolley, excellent cellar. Owner Fredrick Lösel
leads an exemplary front-of-house team. *Specialities* couli-
biac of smoked haddock, gratin of chicken and lobster with
avocado, fricassee of calf's sweetbreads and kidneys, whole
turbotin with Dublin Bay prawns in champagne. ☏

Slough   Holiday Inn

£C 76%

Ditton Road, Langley,
Berkshire. Slough (0753)
44244 ● Map 9C3. Take M4
towards The West. Exit at
junction 5. Hotel is just off the
junction ● Bedrooms 305. En
suite 305. With phone 305.

With TV 305 ● Confirm by 6 ● *Credit* Access, Amex, Diners,
Visa

This fine modern hotel has recently been enhanced by an
extensive refurbishment programme. Decor throughout is
very well coordinated, with pleasing colour combinations and
good attention to detail. There are several lounge areas and
an inviting cocktail bar, and the new leisure complex has its
own bamboo-furnished sitting section. Smartly fitted bedrooms offer excellent up-to-date comforts, and bathrooms
are equipped with hairdryers. *Amenities* garden, sauna,
indoor swimming pool, whirlpool bath, gymnasium, tennis,
dinner-dance (Sat Oct–Jan), 24-hour lounge service, in-house
movies, coffee shop (7am–11.30pm), hairdressing, children's
play area, transport to airport.

Taplow   Cliveden

£A 86%

Near
Maidenhead,
Berkshire.
Burnham
(062 86) 68561
● Map 9B2.
Take M4

towards The West. Exit at junction 7. Take A4 towards
Maidenhead for 2 miles. Turn right just after railway bridge ●
Bedrooms 25. En suite 25. With phone 25. With TV 25 ●
Confirm by arrangement ● *Credit* Access, Amex, Diners,
Visa

This magnificent country house enjoys an incomparable
setting in 400 acres of gardens and woods beside the
Thames. The public rooms, full of paintings and objets d'art,
retain their original splendour – like Nancy Astor's Wedge-
wood blue boudoir, now a restful lounge, and the marvellous
panelled library. Beautiful bedrooms are the epitome of
luxury, with antique furniture, linen sheets and huge bathrooms. The quality of the service is unfortunately not yet on a
par with the splendour of the surroundings. *Amenities* garden,
sauna, outdoor swimming pool, keep-fit equipment, tennis,
squash, coarse fishing, croquet, billiards, 24-hour lounge
service, laundry service, valeting, hotel launch and car.

Taplow   Cliveden Dining Room

Near Maidenhead, Berkshire. Burnham
(062 86) 68561 ● Map 9B2. See hotel entry
above for directions ● Lunch 12.30–2.30.
Dinner 7.30–9.30 ● Set L £26·60. Set D
£35·60. About £85 for two ● *Credit* Access,
Amex, Diners, Visa

An elegant, beautifully proportioned dining room where John
Webber offers nicely composed fixed-price menus for both
lunch and dinner. Typical choices range from asparagus in
puff pastry and foie gras terrine among starters to tender
noisettes of lamb in a smooth pink peppercorn sauce and
fillet steak with onion parcels. Good sweet trolley, plus
excellent coffee and home-made petits fours. Ceremonious
service (with gleaming cloches raised simultaneously from
hot dishes for maximum effect) somewhat marred by the
occasional lapse. A small percentage of the cost of each meal
goes to the National Trust. ☺ ♀ *WELL-CHOSEN* house wine.

West Drayton — Excelsior Hotel

£C
68%

Bath Road, Middlesex. 01-759 6611 ● Map
9D3. Follow signs for Heathrow (M4).
Hotel is close to main entrance ●
Bedrooms 609. En suite 609. With phone
609. With TV 609 ● Confirm by 6 ● *Credit*
Access, Amex, Diners, Visa

Good conference and leisure facilities plus a convenient location close to Heathrow airport make this hotel popular with businessmen, air crews and air travellers alike. Useful shops and a car rental desk create a bright and bustling atmosphere in the smart foyer-lounge and there are two stylish bars. Functional, well-equipped bedrooms include some with superior furnishings and fittings. All have tea-makers, direct-dial phones and colour TVs. Nice modern bathrooms and efficient room service. *Amenities* garden, sauna, outdoor swimming pool, in-house movies, laundry room, valeting, solarium, gymnasium, hairdressing, transport for airport, coffee shop (10am–1am).

West Drayton — Heathrow Park Hotel

£C
59%

Bath Road, Longford, Middlesex. 01-759
2400 ● Map 9D3. Follow signs for
Heathrow (M4). Turn right into Bath Road
(A4) and left into slip road ● Bedrooms
307. En suite 307. With phone 307. With TV
307 ● Confirm by 6 ● *Credit* Access,
Amex, Diners, Visa

This low-rise hotel, once part of the Crest chain, has recently changed hands. It offers practical, up-to-date accommodation in two parallel wings. Bedrooms in the Concorde wing (so called because the hotel is built along Heathrow's longest runway, used by Concorde) are larger and more attractively decorated. All rooms have tea-makers, trouser presses and compact, well-fitted bathrooms. There are two bars – a comfortably furnished public one downstairs and a smartly decorated resident's cocktail bar on the first floor. *Amenities* dinner-dance (Sat), in-house movies, coffee shop (10am–11.30pm), hairdressing, transport for airport, games room.

HOTEL

West Drayton — Holiday Inn

£C 73%

Stockley Road, Middlesex. West Drayton (0895) 445555 ● Map 9D3. Take M4 (Heathrow) to junction 4 and then follow signs for Uxbridge. Take third exit off next roundabout (A408). Hotel is at corner with Cherry Lane ● Bedrooms 400. En suite 400. With phone 400. With TV 400 ● Confirm by 6 ● *Credit* Access, Amex, Diners, Visa

The young, highly professional staff keep standards of housekeeping and service at luxurious levels at this modern hotel. Stylish modern seating sets the tone in the spacious foyer-lounge, in contrast to the heavily-beamed mock-Tudor style of the handsome cocktail bar. Smartly furnished bedrooms are models of thoughtful design, with generous-sized beds and every possible luxury, including the most sumptuous bathrooms. *Amenities* garden, sauna, indoor swimming pool, solarium, keep-fit equipment, 9-hole golf course, tennis, in-house movies, valeting, transport for airport, coffee shop (10.30am–11.30pm), lounge (7am–11.30pm), Prestel.

HOTEL

West Drayton — Post House Hotel

£C 70%

Sipson Road, Middlesex. 01-759 2323 ● Map 9D3. Take M4 (Heathrow) to junction 4 and then follow signs for Staines. Hotel is on left $\frac{1}{4}$ mile from junction 4 ● Bedrooms 582. En suite 582. With phone 582. With TV 582 ● Confirm by 8 ● *Credit* Access, Amex, Diners, Visa.

Conveniently placed for Heathrow airport, this modern high-rise hotel offers a wide range of conference facilities. The stylishly furnished open-plan foyer-lounge leads to an intimate cocktail bar and the pubby Brunel Bar with its heavy engineering theme. Standard bedrooms are also comfortable, with double glazing, air conditioning and mini-bars. Spotless tiled bathrooms. Superior accommodation is offered by Executive Club rooms, which boast their own check-in desk and leisure facilities. *Amenities* garden, sauna, solarium, whirlpool bath, keep-fit equipment, in-house movies, pool table, valeting, transport for airport.

West Drayton   Sheraton-Heathrow Hotel

£C 70%

Bath Road, Middlesex. 01-759 2424 ● Map 9D3. Follow signs for Heathrow (M4). Turn right into

Bath Road (A4). Keep right. Hotel is on right ● Bedrooms 440. En suite 440. With phone 440. With TV 440 ● Confirm by 6 ● *Credit* Access, Amex, Diners, Visa

A low-rise modern hotel to the west of Heathrow airport. Bedrooms (many recently refurbished) are smart and quite stylish with plum and pink decor, and they offer the contemporary comforts of air conditioning and soundproofing, plus accessories like trouser presses and hairdryers. Bathrooms, too, are well fitted. Brass chandeliers and flower-filled urns brighten up the lounge area of the spacious lobby, and the main bar is an intimate relaxing rendezvous. There's also a Victorian pub-style bar in plush red. No dogs. *Amenities* garden, sauna, indoor swimming pool, solarium, coffee shop (6am–11.30pm), in-house movies, hairdressing, transport for airport.

Windsor   Angelo's Wine Bar

5 St Leonards Road, Berkshire. Windsor (0753) 857600 ● Map 9C3. Take M4 to The West. Exit at junction 6. Follow signs for Windsor (A332). At roundabout at end of A332 turn left into Clarence Road. St Leonards Road is fourth turning on right. Wine bar is on left just after traffic lights ● Open noon–2.30 & 6.30–10.30 (Fri & Sat till 11). Closed 25 December ● *Credit* Access, Amex, Diners, Visa

A friendly, relaxed wine bar run with enthusiasm by owner Angelo Delin. Food is a major part of the operation and the menu is prominently displayed on an electronic notice board. There's an excellent choice of carefully cooked dishes: minestrone, mushrooms in red wine and deep-fried squid among the starters; trout bretonne, veal escalope Marsala and chicken breast stuffed with garlic butter as typical main courses. There could even be paella valenciano (for two). Nice sweets, as well, like strawberry gâteau or Dutch apple flan. Friendly, helpful service. No dogs. *Typical prices:* Seafood ayillo £4 Chicken Moscow £6·60. WC

HOTEL

Windsor — Castle Hotel

High Street, Berkshire. Windsor (0753)
851011 ● Map 9C3. Take M4 towards The
West. Exit at junction 6. Follow signs for
Windsor (A332) ● Bedrooms 85. En suite
85. With phone 85. With TV 85 ● Confirm
by 6 ● *Credit* Access, Amex, Diners, Visa

£C
68%

This historic hotel opposite the guildhall is even older than its fine Georgian façade suggests, consisting mainly of two much earlier inns. Fine old oil paintings, elegant furniture and an abundance of fresh flowers grace the beautifully-decorated lounge, with its marbled pillars and rag-painted walls. There's also a pleasant bar. Bedrooms in the main part of the hotel have smart period furniture, those in the annexe have fitted units; all are equipped with direct-dial phones and remote-control TV. Bathrooms are nicely fitted out. *Amenities* coffee shop (10.30am–10.30pm), 24-hour lounge service, laundry service, in-house movies.

JUST A BITE

Windsor — Dôme

5 Thames Street, Berkshire. Windsor
(0753) 864405 ● Map 9C3. Take M4
towards The West. Exit at junction 6.
Follow signs for Windsor (A332). Take first
turning left off A332. Follow signs for town
centre. Turn left at roundabout at end of
Arthur Road, then bear right. Thames
Street is at start of one-way system. Café
is towards top of street, opposite taxi rank
● Open 9–11 (Sun till 10.30). Closed 25
December ● *Credit* Access, Amex, Visa

Only a stone's throw from the castle and with fine views of its massive walls, this is a stylish modern bar-cum-café with conveniently long opening hours. The food is excellent and there is plenty of variety on the menu. including English and continental breakfast, salade niçoise, salmon mousse, croque monsieur and omelettes. Blackboard specials like garlic mushrooms or pork normande supplement the standard fare. Home-made sweets include crème brulée, chocolate mousse and various pastries. Good fresh ingredients, attractive presentation and friendly informal service. Children welcome until 7.30. No dogs. *Typical prices:* Chilli £2·75 Steak sandwich £4·74. WC

HOTEL

Windsor — Oakley Court Hotel

£C 84%

Windsor Road, Berkshire.
Maidenhead (0628) 74141 ●
Map 9C3. Take M4 towards
The West. Exit at junction 6.
Take A355 towards Windsor,
then turn right onto A308 for
Maidenhead. Hotel is
approximately 3 miles down this road ● Bedrooms 91. En
suite 91. With phone 91. With TV 91 ● Confirm by
arrangement ● *Credit* Access, Amex, Diners, Visa

The Gothic mood still prevails in this splendid mansion built in 1859 and set in beautiful gardens bordering the Thames. Rich panelling, fine chandeliers and elegant period furnishings grace the spacious public rooms, including the superb billiards room. Upstairs there are seven luxurious, antique-furnished bedrooms, some with four-posters; the remaining bedrooms are in two modern wings. All have lovely coordinating fabrics, deep-pile carpets and a host of thoughtful extras, from fresh flowers to hairdryers and trouser presses. Excellent bathrooms have telephone extensions. No dogs. *Amenities* garden, coarse fishing, billiards, croquet, pitch & putt, jetty, helipad, laundry service, valeting.

RESTAURANT

Windsor — Oakley Court, Oak Leaf Room

★

Windsor Road, Water Oakley, Berkshire.
Maidenhead (0628) 74141 ● Map 9C3. See
hotel entry above for directions ● Lunch
12.30–2. Dinner 7.30–10 ● Set L £12. Set D
£18 & £30. About £60 for two ● *Credit*
Access, Amex, Diners, Visa

In comfortable though very formal surroundings Murdo MacSween offers modern cooking that really tastes of something: raw materials are excellent, textures terrific, flavours refined yet profound. Two dishes that amply illustrate his skills; ragout of scampi and monkfish with a saffron and Chablis sauce and a puff pastry fleuron; fillet of Scotch beef topped with asparagus and hollandaise, accompanied by a shimmering truffle and Madeira sauce. Crisp vegetables, enticing sweet trolley. *Specialities* beef consommé, terrine of coquilles St Jacques, collops of beef with Stilton and pickled walnuts, chicken suprême with crab. ☺ ♀ *WELL-CHOSEN* house wine.

Windsor   Tracks Brasserie

4 Goswell Hill Arches, Berkshire. Windsor
(0753) 858090 ● Map 9C3. Take M4
towards The West. Exit at junction 6.
Follow signs for Windsor (A332). Take first
turning left off A332. Follow signs for town
centre. Turn left at roundabout into
Goswell Road. The Arches are opposite
car park ● Open noon–2.30 & 6.30–10.45.
Closed Sun & Bank Holidays ● *Credit*
Access, Amex, Diners, Visa

Join the many shoppers, business people and rail travellers
who make tracks for this friendly wine bar-cum-brasserie
occupying one of the cavernous arches beneath Windsor
Central Station. A daily-changing blackboard menu offers a
tempting variety, with taramasalata and creamy home-made
soups, steak and kidney or chicken and mushroom pie,
chargrilled steaks and pork with ginger and orange among
typical offerings. Portions are generous and vegetarians can
usually find something to suit. To finish there are simple
gâteaux, ice creams and sorbets. No dogs. *Typical prices:*
Steak & kidney pie £3·25 Ham & mushroom tagliatelle £3·60.
⊗ WC

Windsor   Windsor Chocolate House

8 Church Street, Berkshire. Windsor
(0753) 860157 ● Map 9C3. Take M4
towards The West. Exit at junction 6.
Follow signs for Windsor (A332). Take first
turning left off A332. Follow signs for town
centre. Turn left off High Street into Castle
Hill. Church Street is second turning on
right ● Open 9.30–5.15. Closed 25 & 26
December ● *Credit* Access, Amex, Diners,
Visa

Just opposite the castle's main entrance – known as the
Henry VIII gateway – is this traditional tea house, which also
does brisk business selling hand-made chocolates and
pastries. Light snacks, including freshly-made sandwiches,
salads and hot pies, are available all day, and at lunchtime
there's a selection of set-price meals. In addition there are
various afternoon teas with good scones and cakes. This is a
busy place and service can seem a little rushed at times.
Unlicensed. No dogs. *Typical prices:* Set lunch of soup,
smoked haddock with pasta & tea £4·95 Set afternoon tea
£3·70. ❤ WC

JUNCTION
–16–

EXIT SIGNS

Travelling clockwise	M40	Oxford
		Uxbridge
		London W
Travelling anticlockwise	M40	Uxbridge
		London
		Oxford

Beaconsfield   Bellhouse Hotel

£C
67%

Oxford Road, Buckinghamshire. Gerrards Cross (0753) 887211 ● Map 9C1. Take M40 west towards Oxford. Exit at junction 2. Follow signs for Beaconsfield (A355), then London A40 ● Bedrooms 118. En suite 118. With phone 118. With TV 118 ● Confirm by 6 ● *Credit* Access, Amex, Diners, Visa

Splendid management and staff keep things running smoothly at this smart modern hotel, where every year one of the Cup Final teams stays on the eve of the big match. New garden-style furniture and a pretty rockery create a relaxing environment in the open-plan foyer-lounge, while the bar is designed around a nautical theme. Bedrooms are most attractively and practically furnished, with stylish fabrics and up-to-date accessories. Many are double-glazed and all have sparkling modern bathrooms. *Amenities* garden, dinner dance (Fri & Sat), in-house movies, pool table, table tennis, 24-hour lounge service.

HOTEL

Burnham — Burnham Beeches Hotel

£D
65%

Grove Road, Buckinghamshire. Burnham (062 86) 3333 ● Map 9B3. Take M40 west towards Oxford. Exit at junction 2. Take A355 towards Slough, ignoring signs for Burnham Beeches. At Farnham Royal turn right at roundabout into Farnham Lane. After one mile turn right at T-junction, then first right again ● Bedrooms 46. En suite 46. With phone 46. With TV 46 ● Confirm by 6 ● *Credit* Access, Amex, Diners, Visa

It's essential to follow the given directions to find this out-of-the-way hotel, a former hunting lodge, where in 1737 Thomas Gray wrote his 'Elegy in a Country Churchyard'. Fine views of the 10 acres of grounds and countryside beyond may be enjoyed from the bedrooms, which are of a decent size and well appointed with reproduction period furniture. No tea- or coffee-making facilities but there is 24-hour room service. The foyer doubles as lounge and bar, and there are good conference facilities. *Amenities* garden, putting, croquet, tennis, games room, in-house movies, laundry service.

HOTEL

Gerrards Cross — Bull Hotel

£C
63%

Oxford Road, Buckinghamshire. Gerrards Cross (0753) 885995 ● Map 9C1. Take M40 west towards Oxford. Exit at junction 2. Follow signs for Beaconsfield (A355), then London A40 ● Bedrooms 40. En suite 40. With phone 40. With TV 40 ● Confirm by arrangement ● *Credit* Access, Amex, Diners, Visa

Old and new combine happily at this long-fronted wayside inn dating from the 17th century. Real fires burn in the old-world bars, where beams and leaded windows create a richly traditional atmosphere. Also in the original building are a few characterful bedrooms, two with four-posters, all with antiques. Other bedrooms, in a modern extension, have fitted units and well-equipped bathrooms; a refurbishment programme is under way to bring their decorations right up-to-date. At the same time, more bedrooms are being built and the already extensive conference facilities expanded. *Amenities* garden, 24-hour lounge service.

Hillingdon — Master Brewer Motel

£D
58%

Western Avenue, Hillingdon Circus,
Middlesex. Uxbridge (0895) 51199 ● Map
9D2. Follow signs for Uxbridge, then
London A40 ● Bedrooms 106. En suite
106. With phone 106. With TV 106 ●
Confirm by 6 ● *Credit* Access, Amex,
Diners, Visa

Practical and neatly maintained, this popular motel has recently been extended to include extra bedroom accommodation. The bustling foyer does double duty as a lounge and is smartly furnished with green-stained bamboo chairs and glass-topped tables. A quieter place to relax may be the cosy bar, where rich chocolate brown furnishings and black marble tables create an intimate atmosphere. Bedrooms are quite separate from the public rooms, being grouped around a central garden with ornamental pool. All have neat fitted units, tea-makers and well-kept bathrooms; most have either patios or balconies. *Amenities* garden, launderette.

Changes in data may occur in
establishments after the Guide goes
to press. Prices should be taken
as indications rather than firm quotes.

JUNCTIONS
17–18

JUNCTION
–18–

EXIT SIGNS

Travelling clockwise	A404	Amersham Chorleywood
Travelling anticlockwise	A404	Amersham Chorleywood Rickmansworth

Amersham   Fripp's

29 The Broadway, Buckinghamshire.
Amersham (024 03) 29370 ● Map 11A4.
Take A404 into Amersham. Follow signs
for Old Amersham. Restaurant is on right
before church ● Open 9.30–5.30, Sun
1.30–6. Closed 25 & 26 December

Dried flowers, beams and pretty green fabrics give a cottage air to this neat restaurant located above a shop on the main road through Amersham. Snacks available all day include freshly made sandwiches with fillings like ham, cheese and tuna, plus ploughman's, salads – made up of any combination you fancy – and nice pastries. Quiche, lasagne and jacket potatoes make an appearance at lunchtime, while the afternoons bring traditional teas with scones and cakes and a choice of three brews – Darjeeling, Earl Grey and Assam. Friendly service. Unlicensed. No dogs. *Typical prices:* Lasagne with salad £2·35 Cream tea £1·15. ⊖ ♥ WC

137

Amersham | Willow Tree

1 Market Square, Buckinghamshire.
Amersham (024 03) 7242 ● Map 11A4.
Take A404 into Amersham. Follow signs
for Old Amersham. Restaurant is on right
by church ● Open Sun–Tues 10–5.30,
Wed–Sat 10–5 & 7.30–9.30. Closed 1
January & 25 & 26 December ● *Credit*
Access, Amex, Diners, Visa

Original beams and bare polished floorboards lend real character to this delightful restaurant on the market square. Superb home-baked goodies – scones, teacakes, flapjacks and pastries – are available all day long, while lunchtime brings such delicious dishes as quail's eggs in blue cheese dressing, smoked trout mousse, chicken in mushroom and mustard sauce and traditional roasts on Sundays. Leave room for a delectable dessert like strawberry meringue. Four evenings a week the menu becomes more ambitious, with dishes like pork medallions with apricots and spinach-wrapped trout fillets. *Typical prices:* Prawn & spinach roulade £3·10 Chinese-style chicken £3·50. ☺ ♨ WC

Chenies | Bedford Arms Thistle Hotel

£C
65%

Near Rickmansworth, Buckinghamshire.
Chorleywood (092 78) 3301 ● Map 11B3.
Take A404 towards Amersham, then B485
into Chenies. Hotel is on right ½ mile
beyond Chorleywood ● Bedrooms 10. En
suite 10. With phone 10. With TV 10 ●
Confirm by 6 ● *Credit* Access, Amex,
Diners, Visa

On the outskirts of the village, this red-brick roadside hotel provides very comfortable accommodation. Smartly fitted bedrooms are of a decent size, neatly kept and well equipped (hairdryers, trouser presses, bath robes, fresh fruit). Bathrooms, too, are splendidly appointed: all are fully tiled and have shower facilities and bidets as well as the usual supply of bath foams and shampoos. Pretty chintz decorations in the lounge convey a quiet, traditional charm. The two public bars with their simple country furniture have a welcoming air, and there's a very smart and attractive cocktail bar. No dogs. *Amenities* garden, in-house movies.

138

Chenies — Bedford Arms Thistle Hotel Restaurant

Near Rickmansworth, Buckinghamshire.
Chorleywood (092 78) 3301 ● Map 11B3.
See hotel entry for directions ● Lunch
12.30–2.30. Dinner 7–10 ● About £50 for
two ● *Credit* Access, Amex, Diners, Visa

Elegant table settings and dark oak panelling set the scene at this formal restaurant overlooking the garden. The menu provides an ample choice of mostly French classics, from onion soup to turbot with hollandaise sauce, veal escalope florentine or steak tartare (ceremoniously prepared at the table). Game is a speciality here and in season you'll find every bird and beast, from roast grouse to jugged hare. Grills are another forte, with virtually any cut of meat or choice of sauce you might fancy. Cooking is basically sound and there's a huge choice of fresh vegetables and fruit. Trolley roast on Sundays. 🄬

Chenies — Bedford Arms Thistle Hotel Bar

(Food)

Near Rickmansworth, Buckinghamshire.
Chorleywood (092 78) 3301 ● Map 11B3.
See hotel entry for directions ● Last bar
food 9.30pm ● *Credit* Access, Amex,
Diners, Visa ● Free House. *Beers* William
Younger's No. 3 Ale, Scotch Bitter, Tartan;
Export; Guinness; Beck's Bier

Even on local hunt days, when thirsty participants throng the two public bars, you can be sure of friendly, efficient service at the Bedford Arms. The menu is varied and interesting, and everything's served in more than ample helpings. Sandwiches (over 30 varieties) are favourite quick bites, and other regular choices run from salade niçoise to sausage and mash. Daily specials might include garlicky grilled sardines and boiled brisket of beef with carrots, dumplings and pease pudding. Familiar desserts like chocolate mousse. Limited choice on Sunday. Children welcome. *Typical prices:* Soft herring roes on toast £3 Hot salt beef sandwich £4·90. 🄬

PUB

Chorleywood — Sportsman Hotel

(B&B)

Station Approach, Hertfordshire.
Chorleywood (092 78) 5155 ● Map 11B4.
Take A404 to Chorleywood. Follow signs
for railway station ● Bedrooms 18. With
bath/shower 18. With TV 18. Check-in all
day ● *Credit* Access, Amex, Diners, Visa ●
Brewery Bass. *Beers* Bass Bitter,
Charrington IPA; Stones Bitter; Guinness;
Carling Black Label; Pilsner; Tennent's
Extra; cider

This imposing late 19th-century hotel standing close to Chorleywood underground station has been recently refurbished and offers splendid bedroom accommodation. All rooms have direct-dial phones, tea-makers, radio-alarms and trouser presses. Most are fitted with modern darkwood units but there's a magnificent bridal suite with elegant four-poster, free-standing pine furniture and romantic furnishings. The basement houses a traditional oak-panelled public bar with ale casks on display and a cheerful open fire. A second, more contemporary bar leads to the patio and garden – the latter incorporating a children's play area with climbing frames, swings and seesaws.

PUB

Ley Hill — Swan Inn

(Food)

Near Chesham, Buckinghamshire.
Chesham (0494) 783075 ● Map 11B3.
Take A404 towards Amersham. Follow
signs for Chenies and Latimer (B485). Turn
left for Ley Hill after Latimer. Pub is on left
● Last bar food 9pm ● *Brewery* Benskins.
Beers Benskins Bitter; Ind Coope Bitter,
Burton Ale; Guinness; Löwenbräu; Skol;
cider

Three centuries ago this pretty inn was a hunting lodge. Now it stands opposite a golf course, set back from the road behind a tiny garden. The bar is full of old-world country charm with its low ceiling, beams and open fire. Rolls, ploughman's and jacket potatoes are popular light bites, while more robust choices could include smoked trout salad, cottage pie, chilli or roast lamb. To finish there are good home-made desserts like tayberry and raspberry crumble or Bakewell tart. Friendly unhurried service. *Typical prices:* Steak pie £2·25 Smoked trout salad £2·40. No bar food Sun eve. 🏠

JUNCTIONS
19–22

JUNCTION –19–

EXIT SIGNS

Travelling clockwise	A41 Watford
Travelling anticlockwise	Hunton Bridge Roundabout

HOTEL

Harrow Weald — Grim's Dyke

£C/D
62%

Old Redding, Middlesex. 01-954 7666 ●
Map 12D5. Take A41 through Watford.
Take A4008 towards Hatch End for 2
miles. Turn left to Harrow Weald ●
Bedrooms 48. En suite 48. With phone 48.
With TV 48 ● Confirm by 7 ● *Credit*
Access, Amex, Diners, Visa ● Closed 25–
30 December

Home for 20 years to Sir William Gilbert, this Tudor-style Victorian mansion designed by Norman Shaw stands in 10 acres of well-kept gardens and woodlands. Gilbert and Sullivan soirées are a Sunday event, and the link is also maintained in public areas like the Yeoman Room, Patience Bar, and Iolanthe Hall with its magnificent alabaster fireplace. Main-house bedrooms are spacious and traditional, annexe rooms are neat and modern. All have tea-making facilities and simply-fitted bathrooms. Major improvements are planned, including a conversion of the terrace into a new lounge. *Amenities* garden, croquet, laundry service.

Watford   Ladbroke Hotel

£C
66%

Elton Way, Hertfordshire. Watford (0923) 35881 ● Map 12B4. Follow signs for Watford and London. Hotel is just beyond junction of M25 and A41 ● Bedrooms 160. En suite 160. With phone 160. With TV 160 ● Confirm by 6 ● *Credit* Access, Amex, Diners, Visa

Comfortable accommodation is offered at this friendly, low-rise modern hotel. Bedrooms are all of a good size and have been recently refurbished with pretty matching curtains and quilted bedcovers. Sixty so-called 'gold star' rooms in addition offer new units and plenty of little extras – ranging from hairdryers and sweets to miniature whiskies and bathtime novelties. Standard rooms, on the other hand, are fully air-conditioned. All have nicely fitted bathrooms. Public areas include a spacious foyer-lounge, comfortable bar and extensive function rooms. *Amenities* dinner dance (Sat), 24-hour lounge service, laundry service, in-house movies.

JUNCTION
–20–

EXIT SIGNS

Travelling clockwise   A41 Aylesbury

Travelling anticlockwise   A41 Aylesbury

JUST A BITE

Berkhamsted — Cook's Delight

★

360 High Street, Hertfordshire.
Berkhamsted (044 27) 3584 ● Map 12A2.
Take A41 towards Aylesbury. Go through
centre of Berkhamsted. Tea room is on
right, about ¼ mile past police station ●
Open Thurs & Fri 10am–9pm, Sat 10–3 &
8pm, Sun noon–5. Closed Mon–Wed, Bank
Holidays (except Good Fri), 1 week August
& 24–30 December ● *Credit* Access, Visa

Tucked away behind a health-food shop, this unassuming little tea room offers superb vegetarian and macrobiotic fare – plus a few poultry dishes for non-vegetarians (no red meat allowed). There's an oriental slant to most of the cooking and organically-grown wholefoods feature prominently. Choose from delicious buckwheat quiches with tasty fillings like cod and celery or spicy turkey, bean casseroles, crunchy salads and wonderfully wholesome sweets – perhaps rhubarb and ginger pie or mango and tofu cheesecake. More elaborate Saturday evening dinner (bookings only). Unlicensed. No smoking. No dogs. *Typical prices:* Vegetarian curry from £3·50 Pumpkin pie £1·50. WC

INN

Berkhamsted — Swan Hotel

£E/F

139 High Street, Hertfordshire.
Berkhamsted (044 27) 71451 ● Map 12A2.
Take A41 (Aylesbury) to Berkhamsted.
Hotel is opposite church ● Bedrooms 19.
En suite 13. With phone 19. With TV 19 ●
Confirm by 6 ● *Credit* Access, Visa

Mine host and wife, Mr and Mrs Caro, extend a warm welcome to all who visit this charming town-centre inn. Travellers have found board and lodging here since the early 17th century and parts of the building date back another 200 years. Bedrooms are all furnished in pleasantly hotchpotch, cottagey style. Thoughtful extras like clothes brushes and manicure sets are provided in addition to tea-making facilities. Front bedrooms are double-glazed. Improvements continue and most rooms now have their own well-fitted shower/bathrooms. There are two cosy bars, as well as a comfortable TV lounge.

Hemel Hempstead	Hemel Hempstead Moat House

£E
56%

London Road, Bourne End, Hertfordshire.
Berkhamsted (044 27) 71241 ● Map 12B2.
Take A41 towards Aylesbury. Do not turn
off for Hemel Hempstead town centre.
Hotel is just beyond railway station ●
Bedrooms 40. En suite 40. With phone 40.
With TV 40 ● Confirm by 7 ● *Credit*
Access, Amex, Diners, Visa ● Closed 24 &
25 December

This low, red-brick hotel stands on the site of an old flour mill and is noted for its modern, award-winning design and delightful riverside location. The design takes the former mill as its theme and from the bright, simply furnished lounge area you can still see the old water wheel breaking the flow of the River Bulbourne. Double glazing is planned for those bedrooms nearest the wheel. All rooms are neatly furnished and have bay windows with attractive pine window seats overlooking the river. TVs, radios, tea-makers and trouser presses are standard equipment. Adequate bathrooms with showers. *Amenities* pool table.

JUNCTION
–21–

EXIT SIGNS

Travelling clockwise	M1 The North
Travelling anticlockwise	M1 The North

PUB

Harpenden   Silver Cup

(Food)

West Common, St Albans Road,
Hertfordshire. Harpenden (058 27) 3095 ●
Map 12C1. Take M1 towards The North.
Exit at junction 10 and follow signs for
Harpenden. Pub is on right on road to St
Albans ● *Credit* Access, Visa ● *Brewery*
Wells. *Beers* Wells Bitter, Bombardier,
Noggin; Guinness; Kellerbräu; Red Stripe;
cider

The name recalls the horse races that used to be run on the common opposite, but you won't be gambling on the quality of the food if you eat at this immensely popular pub. Start with a warming home-made soup, then tuck into generous portions of steak pie, moussaka or rabbit casserole. Or choose avocado followed by a delicious seafood platter. Snacks like ploughman's, pâté, salads and sandwiches leave room for excellent desserts like treacle tart and fresh plum pie. Patio. *Typical prices:* Steak pie & vegetables £2·50 Fish pie £2·50 (No bar food eves, Sun & Bank Holidays). ☺

HOTEL

Hemel Hempstead   Post House Hotel

£C/D
60%

Breakspear Way, Hertfordshire. Hemel
Hempstead (0442) 51122 ● Map 12B2.
Take M1 towards The North. Exit at
junction 8. Hotel is just off junction ●
Bedrooms 107. En suite 107. With phone
107. With TV 107 ● Confirm by 6 ● *Credit*
Access, Amex, Diners, Visa

Behind a rather nondescript exterior the first Post House in Britain still extends a warm welcome to its visitors. Indoor plants and comfortable chairs make for a relaxing reception area, and there's a bright coffee shop as well as the Breakspear Bar, named after the only English pope. Standard bedrooms have neat built-in units, tea-making facilities and well-kept bathrooms with showers. Executive rooms are furnished to a more luxurious standard and offer extras such as trouser presses, direct-dial phones and hairdryers. Efficient, smartly attired staff. *Amenities* garden, 24-hour lounge service, children's play area, coffee shop (10am–10.30pm).

Redbourn	Aubrey Park Hotel

£D
56%

Hemel Hempstead Road, Hertfordshire.
Redbourn (058 285) 2105 ● Map 12C1.
Take M1 towards The North. Exit at
junction 9. Follow signs for Harpenden,
then Redbourn. At Redbourn take B487
towards Hemel Hempstead ● Bedrooms
80. En suite 80. With phone 80. With TV 80
● Confirm by 6 ● *Credit* Access, Amex,
Diners, Visa

A 16th-century house stands at the core of this greatly
extended hotel set in 5 acres of grounds. Dating from this
early period is the heavily beamed upstairs 'Ostlers' Room'
where breakfast is served. Downstairs is a smartly decorated
bar-lounge area with bay windows overlooking the garden
and pool. Over the years blocks of bedrooms have been
added, all joined by enclosed walkways. The rooms them-
selves are simply furnished but all have tea-making facilities,
radios and colour TVs. Executive rooms include extras such
as trouser presses. *Amenities* garden, outdoor swimming
pool, games room, pool table, table tennis, laundry service.

JUNCTION
–21a–

EXIT SIGNS

Travelling clockwise	A405	St Albans London (NW) M1 South
Travelling anticlockwise	A405	Watford Harrow M1

Bricket Wood   Oakwood Tea Room

Oakwood Road, Hertfordshire. Garston
(0923) 674723 ● Map 12C3. Take A405
towards Watford. Turn first left into
Oakwood Road. Tea room is on corner ●
Open 9–5, Sat, Sun & Bank Holidays 10–6.
Closed 2 weeks Christmas

A mother and daughter team are responsible for the goodies at this bright, friendly establishment. They offer a good range of set teas – 'English', with cucumber sandwiches; 'Cream' with light, crumbly, home-made scones but commercially-made jam and aerated cream; and 'Devon', using clotted cream. In addition there's an impressive display of home baking, from creamy cheesecake to treacle tart, coffee and walnut gâteau and seasonal fruit pies. At lunchtime come soup and ploughman's plus a daily hot special like moussaka, steak and kidney pie or cauliflower cheese. Unlicensed. No dogs. *Typical prices:* Ratatouille £1·50 Shepherd's pie £1·50. WC

St Albans   Kingsbury Mill Waffle House

St Michael's Street, Hertfordshire. St
Albans (0727) 53502 ● Map 12C2. Take
A405 to St Albans. Turn left at first
roundabout into Watford Road and then
third left after flyover (King Harry Lane).
Turn right into Blue House Hill (A414) and
first right again ● Open 11–6 (Sun from
noon); in winter 11–5 (Sun from noon).
Closed Mon, Tues & 10 days Christmas

Delicious, freshly baked waffles are the only choice at this ancient mill on the banks of the river Ver. The building, believed to date from Elizabethan times but with the addition of a Georgian facade, is full of character. Inside, you sit on church pews beneath the original beams and enjoy your waffle (plain or whole-wheat) topped with anything from cream cheese with herbs and garlic or ratatouille to black cherries, coconut, banana or chocolate mousse. Minimum charge £1 weekends and Bank Holidays. Unlicensed. No smoking. No dogs. *Typical prices:* Ham, cheese & mushroom waffle £2·50 Banana waffle £1. ☺ ☙ WC

HOTEL

St Albans — Noke Thistle Hotel

£D
69%

Watford Road, Hertfordshire. St Albans
(0727) 54252 ● Map 12C2. Take A405
towards St Albans. Hotel is on left this side
of St Albans ● Bedrooms 57. En suite 57.
With phone 57. With TV 57 ● Confirm by 6
● *Credit* Access, Amex, Diners, Visa ●
Closed 25 & 26 December, 1 & 2 January

With good motorway connections to Luton airport and
London, this smart hotel is popular with both air travellers
and business executives. Standing in well-tended grounds, it
has a pleasantly relaxed atmosphere and a stylish interior
recently extensively refurbished. The reception area retains
the panelled charm of the original house while the modern
open-plan bar-lounge is most attractively furnished with
skilfully coordinated fabrics and deep, comfortable chairs.
Bedrooms are equally pleasing, with subtle pastel colour
schemes and polished darkwood units; all have direct-dial
phones and excellent bathrooms. *Amenities* garden.

JUNCTION
–22–

EXIT SIGNS

Travelling clockwise   A1081   St Albans

Travelling anticlockwise   A1081   St Albans

HOTEL

Harpenden — Glen Eagle Hotel

£D
60%

1 Luton Road, Hertfordshire. Harpenden
(058 27) 60271 ● Map 12C1. Take A1081
through St Albans to Harpenden. Hotel is
on left on far side of Harpenden ●
Bedrooms 51. En suite 51. With phone 51.
With TV 51 ● Confirm by 6 ● *Credit*
Access, Amex, Diners, Visa

Built 60 years ago and still retaining much of its original character, this town-centre hotel offers pleasant overnight accommodation. The wide hall makes an impressive entrance, with the reception tucked away down a corridor to one side. Bedrooms divide into two categories: standard ones are smallish and are fitted with simple units; those designated de luxe are larger and have better-quality, more traditional furniture. All have double glazing, direct-dial phones and private bathrooms with hairdryers. The bar-lounge is an elegant room, and the paved terrace is a popular spot in summer. *Amenities* garden, laundry service.

HOTEL

Harpenden — Harpenden Moat House Hotel

£D
65%

Southdown Road, Hertfordshire.
Harpenden (058 27) 64111 ● Map 12C1.
Take A1081 through St Albans to
Harpenden. Hotel is this side of
Harpenden ● Bedrooms 56. En suite 56.
With phone 56. With TV 56 ● Confirm by 6
● *Credit* Access, Amex, Diners, Visa

The heart of this handsome hotel is a listed Georgian building, where all the distinctly opulent public rooms are housed. These include an elegant pillared foyer-lounge and an eye-catching bar decorated like a campaign tent with a mural of the battle of Gibraltar. Many of the bedrooms in the main house have been smartly refurbished in nicely coordinated colour schemes, and a new block of accommodation promises much style and comfort. Even now, all rooms are well equipped with direct-dial phones, trouser presses and tea-makers, and each has a private bathroom en suite. *Amenities* garden, laundry service.

St Albans   St Michael's Manor Hotel

£D
63%

Fishpool Street, Hertfordshire. St Albans
(0727) 64444 ● Map 12C2. Take A1081
into St Albans. Hotel is SW of city centre,
near the abbey ● Bedrooms 26. En suite
26. With phone 26. With TV 26 ● Confirm
by 6 ● *Credit* Access, Amex, Diners, Visa ●
Closed 27–30 December

Peaceful grounds with a private lake make a pleasant setting for this much-extended manor house with 16th-century origins. A fine galleried staircase dominates the entrance hall, which leads into a cosy little bar fitted with attractive bamboo-style furniture. Both this and the large and comfortable lounge have good views over the lake. Bedrooms are all named after trees and examples of most of these can be seen in the grounds. The rooms are well-maintained and for the most part spacious, with good-quality freestanding furniture, radios, hairdryers and private bath or shower. *Amenities* garden.

St Albans   Sopwell House Hotel

£E
65%

Cottonmill Lane, Hertfordshire. St Albans
(0727) 64477 ● Map 12C2. Take A1081
towards St Albans. Turn off for Sopwell
this side of St Albans ● Bedrooms 30. En
suite 30. With phone 30. With TV 30 ●
Confirm by 6 ● *Credit* Access, Amex,
Diners, Visa ● Closed 27–30 December

Friendly, efficient staff and management are a bonus at this lovely Georgian mansion set in 11 acres of grounds. Handsome public rooms like the welcoming entrance hall, smart cocktail bar and chandelier-hung lounge have an elegant period charm. Bedrooms in the original building are bright and roomy, with fitted units. Those in a newer wing are cosy and modern and another three in a coach-house annexe are full of character. All are equipped with hairdryers and trouser presses and all but one have fully tiled bathrooms with shower units. No dogs. *Amenities* garden, 24-hour lounge service, croquet, laundry service.

JUNCTIONS 23–24

JUNCTION
–23–

EXIT SIGNS

Travelling clockwise	A1 (M)	Hatfield
	A1081	Barnet London (NW)
Travelling anticlockwise	A1 (M)	Hatfield
	A1081	Barnet London (NW)

Hatfield   Comet Hotel

£D
61%

301 St Albans Road West, Hertfordshire.
Hatfield (070 72) 65411 ● Map 13C3. Take
A1(M) north towards Hatfield. Hotel is at
junction of A1(M) and A414 to Hatfield ●
Bedrooms 57. En suite 57. With phone 57.
With TV 57 ● Confirm by 6 ● *Credit*
Access, Amex, Diners, Visa

The aircraft industry once prospered around here, and this
popular hotel takes its name from the 1934 De Havilland
Comet Racer. Viewed from above, the shape of the original
building follows the lines of the plane. Inside, public areas
such as the Mosquito Bar are still named after locally-built
aircraft, and a few old prints also recall the 1930s. However,
there's little nostalgia in the newly-completed bar-lounge with
its smart contemporary decor and comfortable modern
furnishings. Roomy bedrooms are all neatly fitted, having
armchairs and an occasional table, plus tea-makers, trouser
presses and well-equipped bathrooms. *Amenities* garden.

HOTEL

RESTAURANT

Old Hatfield · Salisbury

★

15 The Broadway, Hertfordshire. Hatfield
(070 72) 62220 ● Map 13C2. Take A1(M)
north towards Hatfield, then A414 to
Hatfield. Turn right onto A1000 and follow
signs for Old Hatfield and Hatfield House ●
Lunch 12.30–2. Dinner 7.30–9.30 ● Set L
£9·75 & £11·50. Set D £19·50. About £52
for two ● *Credit* Access, Amex, Diners,
Visa ● Closed L Sat, D Sun, all Mon &
Bank Holidays

Julian Waterer is the genius behind the delightful meals enjoyed at this charming restaurant. Each course is a marvel of meticulous preparation in the modern style. Herbs highlight tastes, pastrywork is noteworthy, presentation quite breath-taking. Some fine wines at high prices. *Specialities* smoked duck, asparagus and pink grapefruit salad in a pine kernel dressing, salmon and herring roes with ginger and lime sabayon and mange-touts, served under a pastry crust, medallions of lamb with a courgette purée on green pepper-corn hollandaise, terrine of white and dark chocolate in a rum sauce with oranges. ☺ ♀ *WELL-CHOSEN* house wine.

HOTEL

South Mimms · Crest Hotel

£C
60%

Bignells Corner, Near Potters Bar,
Hertfordshire. Potters Bar (0707) 43311 ●
Map 13B4. Take B197 towards North
Mimms. Hotel is on right ● Bedrooms 120.
En suite 120. With phone 120. With TV 120
● Confirm by 6 ● *Credit* Access, Amex,
Diners, Visa

A splendidly-equipped leisure centre is the main attraction at this modern, low-rise hotel. Public areas are bright and welcoming. Bedrooms have functional fitted furniture and neat, compact bathrooms, plus a good range of extras, from fresh fruit and mineral water to hairdryers and evening paper. Four special rooms set aside for ladies offer glossy maga-zines, doors with spy-holes, dressing gowns and tea-trays laid with pretty Wedgwood china. Another room has a jacuzzi. *Amenities* garden, indoor swimming pool, keep-fit equipment, sauna, solarium, snooker, pool table, children's playground, coffee shop (9.30am–6.30pm), laundry service.

Welwyn   Heath Lodge Hotel

£D/E
60%

Danesbury Park Road, Hertfordshire.
Welwyn (043 871) 7064 ● Map 13C1. Take
A1(M) north towards Hatfield. Follow signs
for Welwyn (A1000), then for Stevenage
and Knebworth (B197). Take second left
into Canonsfield Road. Bear left at top of
hill and first left again. Hotel is 400 yards
down on left ● Bedrooms 32. En suite 32.
With phone 32. With TV 32 ● Confirm by 6
● *Credit* Access, Amex, Diners, Visa

Standing in well-tended grounds, this comfortable hotel is maintained to high standards throughout. Public areas include a warmly decorated lounge with polished parquet floor and scattered rugs, a cosy little bar and a delightful sun lounge with pretty floral-print furnishings and picture windows overlooking the gardens. A few bedrooms are on the first floor of the main house but most are located in long, low motel-style blocks ranged around three sides of a grassy quadrangle. All have good modern furnishings, direct-dial phones, remote-control TVs, radio consoles, tea-makers and bathrooms with shower facilities. *Amenities* garden.

Welwyn   Heath Lodge Hotel Restaurant

Danesbury Park Road, Hertfordshire.
Welwyn (043 871) 7064 ● Map 13C1. See
hotel entry above for directions ● Lunch
12.30–2. Dinner 7–9.30, Sun 7–9 ● Set L &
D from £8·95. About £42 for two ● *Credit*
Access, Amex, Diners, Visa ● Closed L Sat

Interesting dishes in the modern French style are the speciality of this well-run restaurant. Careful preparation and thoughtful presentation make for finely-flavoured, artistic results. Appetising starters might include chicken pâté with raspberry jelly, fresh salmon terrine with watercress sauce and potted mussels with avocado coulis. To follow there are mouth-watering combinations like breast of duck with fresh figs, rolled salmon trout with bourguignon sauce and breast of chicken in a pastry case with truffle sauce. Tempting desserts range from hot mandarin soufflé to meringues with hot chocolate sauce. For Sunday lunch there's a choice of two traditional roasts. ☻

Welwyn Garden City — Crest Hotel

£C/D
59%

Homestead Lane, Welwyn Garden City,
Hertfordshire. (07073) 24336 ● Map 13C2.
Take A1(M) north towards Hatfield. Take
A414 through Hatfield towards Hertford.
Turn left onto A1000 and follow signs for
Queen Elizabeth II Hospital. Turn left into
Hollybush Lane, then second right ●
Bedrooms 58. En suite 58. With phone 58.
With TV 58 ● Confirm by 6 ● *Credit*
Access, Amex, Diners, Visa

It's essential to follow the directions given here to find this modern red-brick hotel on the outskirts of town. Even then, among all the red-brick houses, it may still be hard to spot. The bar-lounge with comfortable bamboo-style furniture is a pleasant place to relax with a drink and there are useful function and meeting facilities. Bedrooms (six designated non-smoking) provide roomy, practical accommodation, with built-in furniture, tea-makers and trouser presses. Two single rooms have showers only; the rest have good-sized bathrooms with shower facilities. *Amenities* garden, in-house movies, laundry service.

JUNCTION
–24–

EXIT SIGNS

Travelling clockwise	A111	Potters Bar
Travelling anticlockwise	A111	Potters Bar

Hadley Wood   West Lodge Park

£C/D
65%

Cockfosters Road, Near Barnet,
Hertfordshire. 01-440 8311 ● Map 13C4.
Take A111 south towards Cockfosters.
Hotel is signposted ● Bedrooms 50. En
suite 50. With phone 50. With TV 50 ●
Confirm by arrangement ● *Credit* Access,
Amex, Diners, Visa

Enjoying a commanding hilltop position and surrounded by 32 acres of landscaped grounds with lake and arboretum, this mansion dates back to the early 16th century. It was rebuilt during the reign of William IV and more recent additions are in the same early 19th-century style. The day rooms are mainly traditional in character, with many fine English paintings, though the bar has a more modern appeal. Bedrooms are spacious and generally well-kept, with free-standing furniture and nicely equipped bathrooms. Attention needed to housekeeping and maintenance in public areas. No dogs. *Amenities* garden, croquet, putting, helipad, laundry service.

Newgate Street   Ponsbourne Hotel

£E
66%

Ponsbourne Park, Near Hertford,
Hertfordshire. Cuffley (0707) 875221 ●
Map 13D3. Take A10 towards Hertford.
Follow signs for Cuffley (B198 and then
B156). Turn right by monument at top of
Goffs Lane into Newgate Street Road.
Turn left into Darnicle Hill for Newgate
Street. Hotel is on left before village centre
● Bedrooms 32. En suite 32. With phone
32. With TV 32 ● Confirm by 9 ● *Credit*
Access, Amex, Diners, Visa

Impressive leisure and conference facilities attract holiday-makers and business visitors alike to this rambling Victorian mansion, set in extensive grounds. Five new tennis courts are the latest amenity to join the list of sporting options. A replica of the Lourdes grotto graces the Garden Room – recalling the time when the house was used as a Roman Catholic convent – and there are several other rather more conventional lounges and a bar. Cheerful, roomy bedrooms have radios, tea-makers and modern bath/shower rooms. *Amenities* garden, outdoor swimming pool, pitch & putt, games room, pool table, table tennis, laundry service, teletext.

JUNCTIONS
25–27

JUNCTION
–25–

EXIT SIGNS

Travelling clockwise	A10	Hertford
		Enfield
Travelling anticlockwise	A10	Enfield
		Hertford

Hertford   Marquee

1 Bircherley Green, Hertfordshire.
Hertford (0992) 558999 ● Map 14A1. Take
A10 and A414 to Hertford. Head for town
centre, follow system round and turn off
for Bircherley Green car park ● Lunch 12–
2.30. Dinner 7–10.30, Sun 7–10 ● Set L
Mon–Fri £7·50. About £45 for two ● *Credit*
Access, Amex, Diners, Visa ● Closed
Good Friday

Imaginative modern cooking in a flamboyantly decorated
restaurant on two floors. The decorative theme – from which
the establishment takes its name – is a Napoleonic tent. The
upper room is particularly stylish, with orange-curtained walls
and a draped and pleated ceiling; downstairs the theme
continues in pink and grey. The cooking itself varied on our
visit, some dishes being really excellent, notably a very fine
scallop mousseline with orange sauce. Note hot foie gras,
chicken breast stuffed with cèpes and some nice sweets like
wine-poached pears with pear and raspberry sorbets. Fine
selection of classic French wines. ♀ *WELL-CHOSEN* house
wine. ☕

HOTEL

Hertingfordbury — White Horse Inn

£D
61%

Hertingfordbury Road, Hertfordshire.
Hertford (0992) 56791 ● Map 14A1. Take
A10 and A414 to Hertford. Continue on
A414 for 2 miles to Hertingfordbury ●
Bedrooms 42. En suite 42. With phone 42.
With TV 42 ● Confirm by 6 ● *Credit*
Access, Amex, Diners, Visa

Set in attractive and well-tended gardens in the village centre,
the White Horse was a 16th-century farmhouse before it
became a coaching inn. Although well-modernised, and with
a new block of bedrooms just completed, it retains much of
the building's original character. A gas-fired 'open log' fire
burns in the central brick hearth of the comfortably-furnished
bar-lounge, creating a warm and welcoming atmosphere.
Bedrooms are furnished mainly with darkwood units; a few
have imported Italian pieces. All have tea-makers, remote-
control TVs and well-equipped bathrooms with shower
facilities. *Amenities* garden.

JUST A BITE

Ware — Ben's Brasserie Bar

14 High Street, Hertfordshire. Ware (0920)
68383 ● Map 14B1. Take A10 towards
Hertford. Follow signs for Ware town
centre. Brasserie is on right of High Street
directly after bridge ● Open noon–2.30 &
6–11. Closed Sun, Bank Holidays & 4 days
Christmas

Cooking and presentation both shine at this friendly brasserie
and bar on the site of an old pub. Make your choice from the
display counter – quiche, Scotch eggs, terrine, salads – or
consult the blackboard for hot dishes like moules marinière,
spicy meatballs and fresh fillets of haddock. Sweets might
include coffee and banana gâteau, coconut tart and orange
cheesecake with a smooth orange sauce. Owners take an
active interest in day-to-day running of place, planning menus
and experimenting with new dishes. No children in the
evening. No dogs. *Typical prices:* Chicken au poivre £2·95
Moules marinière £2·45. ⊖ WC

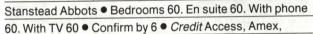

Ware — Briggens Hotel

£D 73%

Stanstead Road, Near
Stanstead Abbots,
Hertfordshire. Roydon
(027979) 2416 ● Map 14B1.
Take A10 towards Hertford,
then A414 towards Harlow.
Hotel is a mile beyond

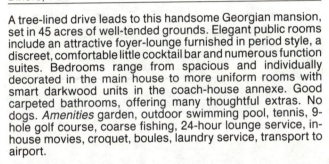

Stanstead Abbots ● Bedrooms 60. En suite 60. With phone
60. With TV 60 ● Confirm by 6 ● *Credit* Access, Amex,
Diners, Visa

A tree-lined drive leads to this handsome Georgian mansion,
set in 45 acres of well-tended grounds. Elegant public rooms
include an attractive foyer-lounge furnished in period style, a
discreet, comfortable little cocktail bar and numerous function
suites. Bedrooms range from spacious and individually
decorated in the main house to more uniform rooms with
smart darkwood units in the coach-house annexe. Good
carpeted bathrooms, offering many thoughtful extras. No
dogs. *Amenities* garden, outdoor swimming pool, tennis, 9-
hole golf course, coarse fishing, 24-hour lounge service, in-
house movies, croquet, boules, laundry service, transport to
airport.

Ware — Sunflowers

7 Amwell End, Hertfordshire. Ware (0920)
3358 ● Map 14B1. Take A10 towards
Hertford and follow signs for Ware. Turn
right at the mini-roundabout at entrance to
town, then left into Amwell End.
Restaurant is on left ● Open 10–5 (Thurs
till 1.30). Closed Sun & Bank Holidays

This friendly, well managed establishment, run in tandem with
a wholefood shop on the ground floor, started off as just a
takeaway service but soon developed into a sit-down
restaurant on the first floor. The healthy vegetarian menu
includes vegeburgers, salads, jacket potatoes and a popular
risotto with sunflower seeds, corn, peas and brown rice.
Organically grown vegetables are used whenever possible,
and soya milk is offered with tea. Don't miss the special
sunflower scones filled with sugarless jam and Greek yoghurt.
Unlicensed. No smoking. No dogs. *Typical prices:* Carrot &
lentil soup 65p Butter bean ratatouille £1·50. WC

JUNCTION
–26–

EXIT SIGNS

Travelling clockwise	A121	Waltham Abbey Loughton
Travelling anticlockwise	A121	Waltham Abbey Loughton

Epping — Post House Hotel

£C/D
62%

High Road, Bell Common, Essex. Epping (0378) 73137 ● Map 14C3. Take A121 towards Loughton. Turn left onto B1393 towards Epping. Hotel is on this side of Epping ● Bedrooms 82. En suite 82. With phone 82. With TV 82 ● Confirm by 6 ●
Credit Access, Amex, Diners, Visa

Lavish refurbishment continues apace at this converted coaching inn at Bell Common, behind the old 'Bell Inn' sign. Smart darkwood furnishings and handsome fabrics have brightened up the foyer-lounge, and the old-world bar has been similarly transformed. Bedrooms are located in modern motel-style blocks. Standard rooms are comfortably and stylishly furnished and have direct-dial phones and tea-makers. Executive rooms are altogether more luxurious and offer hairdryers and trouser presses. All bathrooms have shower facilities; those in executive category are supplied with usual range of extras. *Amenities* garden, children's play area, 24-hour lounge service, in-house movies.

South Woodford   Ho-Ho

20 High Road, Essex. 01-989 1041 ● Map
14B5. Take A121 towards Loughton. Turn
right onto A104 for Woodford Green. Take
A11 towards Wanstead. Restaurant is on
left ● Lunch 12–3. Dinner 6–11.30 ● Set L
from £5. Set D from £9·50. About £35 for
two ● *Credit* Access, Amex, Diners, Visa ●
Closed 25 & 26 December

Manager Steve Man leads a smiling, attentive service team at this delightful Chinese restaurant, where cut flowers, spotless pink tablecloths and smartly tiled floors create a fresh and appealing ambience. The menu is easy to understand and takes in all the main regional cuisines – Pekingese, Szechuan, Cantonese – as well as a few Malaysian dishes. Cooking is meticulous and timing impeccable. Specialities range from hot and sour soup or crispy seaweed with grated scallops to chilli prawns with water chestnuts or steamed whole sea bass with ginger and spring onions. Glazed toffee apples to finish. ♀ *WELL-CHOSEN* house wine.

Toot Hill   Green Man

(Food)

Near Ongar, Essex. North Weald (037 882)
2255 ● Map 14D3. Take A121 towards
Loughton and follow signs for Epping
(B1393). Turn right into Station Road and
first left after the flyover (M11). Follow road
for 3 miles ● Last bar food 10pm ● *Credit*
Access, Diners, Visa ● *Brewery* Watneys.
Beers Webster's Yorkshire Bitter; Combes
Bitter; Ben Truman; Watneys Dark Mild;
Guinness; Carlsberg; cider

The flower-filled front patio of this pleasant, creeper-clad pub is just the place on a fine summer's day to sample John Rhodes' excellent champagnes. His food is a treat at any time of year, and in the comfortable bar you can tuck into appetising dishes like veal Kiev, grilled sardines and Mexican chicken, as well as standard soups, salads and sandwiches. Wholesome desserts might include fresh blackberry cheesecake. Excellent wines to accompany the more substantial dishes. Herbs all home-grown in the garden. Children welcome. *Typical prices:* Veal Kiev with vegetables £4·75 Liver & bacon with vegetables £3·50. ✆

PUB

RESTAURANT

Waltham Abbey   Blunk's

20 Market Square, Essex. Lea Valley
(0992) 712352 ● Map 14B3. Take A121
into Waltham Abbey. Market Square is
behind the abbey ● Lunch 12.30–2.30.
Dinner 7.30–11.30 ● Set L & D £20 inc.
wine. About £50 for two ● *Credit* Access,
Amex, Diners, Visa

A long list of expertly prepared French dishes constitutes the
main menu in this agreeable restaurant. Chef Pièrre Mauroux
maintains reliably high standards in the kitchen he has
directed for eight years: ingredients are carefully selected,
sauces lovingly nurtured, dishes attractively though simply
presented. Seafood is much favoured, with delights like sole
Newburg, turbot florentine and a very fine coquille de fruits
de mer. Plenty of meat, too, including beef Stroganoff and
breast of chicken with a whisky-zipped sauce. Home-made
ice-cream forms the basis of many of the desserts (peach
melba, pears Belle Hélène, etc.). ♀ *WELL-CHOSEN* house
wine. ☺

JUNCTION
–27–

EXIT SIGNS

Travelling clockwise	M11	London (NE) Harlow Cambridge Stansted Airport
Travelling anticlockwise	M11	Harlow Cambridge London (NE) Stansted Airport The North via M11 & A1

Harlow — Harlow Moat House

£D/E
60%

Southern Way, Essex. Harlow (0279)
22441 ● Map 14C2. Take M11 north
towards Harlow. Exit at junction 7. Take
A414 towards Harlow. Hotel is on this side
of Harlow ● Bedrooms 120. En suite 120.
With phone 120. With TV 120 ● Confirm by
6 ● *Credit* Access, Amex, Diners, Visa

A modern hotel, well-maintained and efficiently run, that has recently benefited from a very successful refurbishment programme. New lightwood units, pretty curtains and luxury deep-pile carpets are among the many improvements to be found in the redesigned bedrooms, all of which have remote-control TVs, tea-makers and trouser presses. Neat, compact bathrooms throughout. There's a spacious foyer-lounge with smartly tiled floor and a restyled rustic bar. Newly appointed function rooms have excellent facilities and a handsome reception area all of their own. *Amenities* garden, dancing (Sat), 24-hour lounge service, laundry service, games room.

Old Harlow — Green Man Hotel

£D
62%

Mulberry Green, Essex. Harlow (0279)
442521 ● Map 14C1. Take M11 north
towards Harlow. Exit at junction 7. Take
A414 towards Harlow. Follow signs for Old
Harlow ● Bedrooms 55. En suite 55. With
phone 55. With TV 55 ● Confirm by 6 ●
Credit Access, Amex, Diners, Visa

This ancient inn, a listed building dating from the 14th century, is tucked away by the village green in a quiet backwater of Harlow new town. It retains plenty of old-world charm in its two bars, with their bare brick walls, dark beams and panelling, and old brasses. The reception area by contrast is strikingly up-to-date. Bedrooms, housed in a separate block, are also thoroughly modern, with smart darkwood units and gadgets like tea-makers and radio-alarms. All have compact, fully tiled bathrooms. Smart, friendly staff. Fresh flowers everywhere create a welcoming impression. *Amenities* garden.

HOTEL

Woodford Bridge   Prince Regent Hotel

£D/E
57%

Manor Road, Essex. 01-504 7635 ● Map
14C5. Take M11 south towards London
NE. Exit at junction 4. Take A406 (North
Circular) west to roundabout. Double back
on A406 heading east. Turn left onto A113.
Turn right at Woodford Bridge onto B173.
Hotel is on right ● Bedrooms 10. En suite
10. With phone 10. With TV 10 ● Confirm
by arrangement ● *Credit* Access, Amex,
Diners, Visa

Set well back from the road, this small Georgian hotel has
plenty of period furnishings to enhance the character of its
public rooms. Huge crystal chandeliers light the entrance hall
and staircase while smart, blue-upholstered reproduction
French chairs look quite at home beneath the lofty ceilings.
Eighteenth-century portraits and Victorian watercolours complete the picture. Only the mellow, club-like bar is slightly out
of character. Neat, prettily fitted modern bedrooms provide
tea-making facilities and radio-alarms, and all have tiled,
carpeted bathrooms with shower units. Friendly though
sometimes casual service. No dogs. *Amenities* garden,
laundry service, cabaret.

HOTEL

Woodford Green   Woodford Moat House

£D
62%

Oak Hill, Essex. 01-505 4511 ● Map 14B4.
Take M11 south towards London NE. Exit
at junction 4. Take A406 (North Circular)
west. Take A104 towards Woodford
Green. Turn left for Oak Hill ● Bedrooms
99. En suite 99. With phone 99. With TV 99
● Confirm by 6 ● *Credit* Access, Amex,
Diners, Visa

Handily placed for the major road network, this modern
businessman's hotel is also close to the peace of Epping
Forest. The building is about 15 years old, with a new wing
added within the last 4 years. Bedrooms are decorated in
warm colour schemes and simply furnished with wood-effect
laminate units. All have tea-makers, remote-control TVs and
en suite bathrooms. The huge foyer doubles as a comfortable
lounge, with caramel-coloured velour upholstery comple-
menting the plain brown brick walls and creating a stylish and
relaxing ambience. There's also a pleasant, discreetly lit bar
with cane furniture. *Amenities* laundry service.

JUNCTIONS
28–31

JUNCTION
–28–

EXIT SIGNS

Travelling clockwise	A12	Chelmsford Romford
	A1023	Brentwood
Travelling anticlockwise	A12	Chelmsford
	A1023	Brentwood East Anglia via A12

Billericay | Webber's Wine Bar

2 Western Road, Essex. Billericay (027 74) 56581 ● Map 15D4. Take A1023 through Brentwood. At Shenfield take A129 to Billericay. In town centre turn left at traffic lights into High Street. Turn left again at third set of traffic lights into Western Road. Wine bar is on right ● Open 11–2.30 & 6–10.30 (Mon from 7, Fri & Sat till 11). Closed Sun, Bank Holiday lunches, 2 weeks July–August & 10 days Christmas ● *Credit* Access, Amex, Diners, Visa

Splendid preparation and presentation distinguish the excellent food at this lively wine bar. Sit up at the bar or wait for a table and tuck into cold meats, raised pies, pâtés and salads from the display counter, or opt for a blackboard special such as haunch of venison. Mediterranean fish soup, crab quiche, chilli and jacket potatoes are regular stalwarts, and there are irresistible desserts like raspberry and hazelnut syllabub and sticky toffee pudding. Minimum charge of £5 Friday and Saturday evenings. No dogs. *Typical prices:* Soup of the day £1·95 Shredded smoked chicken with French beans £4·25. ☙ WC

HOTEL

Brentwood — Brentwood Moat House

£C
67%

London Road, Essex. Brentwood (0277)
225252 ● Map 15B4. Follow signs for
Brentwood. Hotel is on right,
$\frac{1}{4}$ mile from junction ● Bedrooms 38. En
suite 38. With phone 38. With TV 38 ●
Confirm by 6 ● *Credit* Access, Amex,
Diners, Visa

This welcoming hotel is an authentic Tudor hunting lodge, once associated with Catherine of Aragon and later mentioned in Pepys's diary. Period features in the public areas are carefully preserved, notably the handsome carved ceiling and arched stone fireplace in the lounge and the beams and diamond-pane windows in the bar. The panelled Henry VIII room makes an impressive conference venue. Bedrooms in the main house are really suites, with separate sitting areas and antique furniture. Those in the modern garden wing have fitted units. Neat modern bathrooms throughout. *Amenities* garden, 24-hour lounge service, laundry service, baby listening.

Brentwood — Post House Hotel

£C/D
60%

Brook Street, Essex. Brentwood (0277)
210888 ● Map 15B4. Follow signs for
Brentwood. Hotel is on right, this side of
Brentwood ● Bedrooms 120. En suite 120.
With phone 120. With TV 120 ● Confirm by
6 ● *Credit* Access, Amex, Diners, Visa

This purpose-built hotel is popular both for an overnight stop and as a conference centre. Comfortable leather-look seating and modern prints give a smart, contemporary feel to the spacious foyer-lounge area and the cocktail bar is equally stylish. A second bar is simpler and has a more pub-like atmosphere. Standard bedrooms have bright airy colour schemes and are equipped with tea-makers, radios and mini-bars. All have neat, attractively tiled bathrooms. Executive bedrooms, with smart darkwood units, offer a whole range of extras including complimentary evening paper. *Amenities* garden, outdoor swimming pool, laundry service, coffee shop (7am–10pm).

HOTEL

HOTEL

Ingatestone Heybridge Moat House Hotel

£D
68%

Roman Road, Essex. Ingatestone (0277)
355355 ● Map 15C3. Follow signs for
Chelmsford. Turn onto B1002 towards
Ingatestone. Hotel is signposted ●
Bedrooms 22. En suite 22. With phone 22.
With TV 22 ● Confirm by arrangement ●
Credit Access, Amex, Diners, Visa

Incorporating a tithe barn dating back to 1494, this comfortably modernised hotel is a popular venue for functions and conferences. Bedrooms in a recently built single-storey annexe approached via a covered walkway are smartly and thoughtfully designed, with comfortable beds, modern modular furniture and plenty of writing space. All have remote-control TVs, direct-dial phones, hairdryers, trouser presses and well-fitted private bathrooms. There is one luxury 'suite' and another room specially adapted for disabled guests. Public areas include a cosy cocktail bar with wood panelling and leather chairs. No dogs. *Amenities* dancing (Thurs–Sat).

JUNCTION
–29–

EXIT SIGNS

Travelling clockwise	A127	Basildon Southend
Travelling anticlockwise	A127	Romford Basildon Southend

HOTEL

Basildon   Crest Hotel

£C/D
59%

Cranes Farm Road, Essex. Basildon
(0268) 3955 ● Map 15D5. Follow signs for
Basildon (A127, then A176). Take A1235
signposted Industrial Estate. Hotel is on
left ● Bedrooms 116. En suite 116. With
phone 116. With TV 116 ● Confirm by 6 ●
Credit Access, Amex, Diners, Visa

A modern hotel pleasantly situated by an artificial lake. The
leafy foyer-lounge is bright and airy and leads to a relaxing
conservatory bar, which has stylish cane furniture and a good
view over the lake. For guests who prefer something more
lively, 'Sam's Grand Slam Bar' at the other end of the building
provides plenty of loud music. There are several conference
suites. Bedrooms and bathrooms are appointed in neat,
practical style. Guests may use the facilities of a nearby
country club. *Amenities* garden, putting, games room, pool
table, dinner dance (Sat), laundry service, 24-hour lounge
service, baby listening.

JUNCTION
–30–

EXIT SIGNS

Travelling clockwise	A13	Dagenham Grays Tilbury (A1036, A126) (A1090)
Travelling anticlockwise	A13	East Grays Tilbury

Grays   R. Mumford & Son

6 Cromwell Road, Essex. Grays Thurrock
(0375) 374153 ● Map 15B7. Take A13 into
Grays. Turn left at beginning of one-way
system. Restaurant is opposite the
Thameside Theatre ● Open 11.45–2.15 &
5.30–11. Closed Sun, Bank Holidays
(except Good Fri) & 10 days Christmas

This bright, modern fish restaurant with smart green canopy
doubles as a takeaway fish bar. Watch the blackboard for
seasonal daily specials like crab, lobster and salmon. Other
equally tasty choices include market-fresh cod, plaice, halibut
and skate, lightly battered and served with jumbo chips or a
crisp salad. Steak and chicken are also available, plus
seafood and cottage cheese salads and simple starters like
soup, pâté and smoked salmon. Home-made fresh-cream
sweets include Black Forest gâteau and sherry trifle. Charming service. Minimum charge £2·50. No dogs. *Typical prices:*
Skate & chips £3·50 Chicken salad £2·70. WC

North Stifford   Stifford Moat House

£D
61%

High Road, Near Grays, Essex. Grays
Thurrock (0375) 371451 ● Map 15B6. Take
A13 to exit signposted Grays. Hotel is just
off this junction on A1012 towards North
Stifford ● Bedrooms 64. En suite 64. With
phone 64. With TV 64 ● Confirm by
arrangement ● *Credit* Access, Amex,
Diners, Visa ● Closed 2 days Christmas

This converted Georgian house enjoys a peaceful and
secluded setting. The lounge has five period windows
overlooking the garden and there's an agreeable panelled
bar facing a courtyard. The conference suites are also in the
original building. Bedrooms are in two modern extensions
and have practical fitted units (with good writing surfaces),
tea-makers and spotless bathrooms. All benefit from an
impressive direct-dial telephone system which can store
personal messages and obey a variety of push-buttoned
instructions. Staff are friendly and helpful. *Amenities* garden,
croquet, pitch & putt, tennis, pétanque, children's play area,
dinner dance (Sat), 24-hour lounge service.

Index

Index